General Practitioners Handbook

Second edition

NORMAN ELLIS
Under Secretary, British Medical Association

DAVID GRANTHAM
Industrial Relations Officer, British Medical Association

Foreword by

JOHN CHISHOLM
Chairman, General Practitioners Committee,
British Medical Association

RADCLIFFE MEDICAL PRESS

Radcliffe Medical Press Ltd
18 Marcham Road, Abingdon, Oxon OX14 1AA

First edition 1997

British Library Cataloguing in Publication Data

A catalogue record for this book is available from the British Library.

ISBN 1 85775 406 9

Typeset by Advance Typesetting Ltd, Oxfordshire
Printed and bound by TJ International Ltd, Padstow, Cornwall

Contents

Foreword

This book explains in clear and concise terms the business side of general practice. It provides an important reference document for any practice and is particularly relevant to the needs of younger principals, GP registrars and other doctors who have recently entered general practice. Each chapter provides a useful account of a key facet of general practice and tells the reader how to obtain further advice and assistance.

JOHN CHISHOLM
Chairman
General Practitioners Committee
British Medical Association
November 1999

Preface

This is the second edition of the BMA's *General Practitioners Handbook*. It is directly relevant to both GPs and their practice staff, particularly those who have recently entered general practice, such as GP registrars, newly appointed GP principals and newly appointed staff. While the book brings together factual accounts of several key aspects of the business side of general practice, its overriding aim is to describe clearly and concisely the principles and rules governing the business side of general practice. As the book provides an outline and summary of its various subjects, the reader is told at the beginning of each chapter where to go for further information, advice and assistance.

The term 'health authority' is used generically and applies to health authorities in England and Wales and health boards in Scotland and Northern Ireland.

NORMAN ELLIS
DAVID GRANTHAM
November 1999

1 Contractual options in general practice

Where to obtain advice and assistance

BMA members can contact their local BMA office for expert advice and assistance. Help can also be obtained from health authority and local medical committee (LMC) offices. The BMA web site is at www.bma.org.uk

Further reading includes Ellis N and Chisholm J (1997) *Making Sense of the Red Book* (3e). Radcliffe Medical Press, Oxford, the Red Book itself and the NHS (General Medical Services) Regulations 1992.

There are various options for doctors wishing to work in general practice. A majority are GP principals who work as independent contractors to the NHS. The rest are non-principals working in a variety of contractual arrangements, including locums, assistants, associates, retainees and doctors involved in Primary Care Act pilot schemes.

GP principals and the independent contractor status

An overwhelming majority of doctors working in general practice are GP principals working as independent contractors. An independent contractor is a self-employed person who has entered into a contract for services with another party. This contract for services is fundamentally different from the contract of service which governs the more usual employee–employer relationship. A key test, often used to distinguish between these two types of contract, relates to the question of 'control'. Generally, the more control A exercises over B's work, the more likely A is to be the employer and B the employee. Thus, if A can tell B not only what job to do but how it is to be done, A has sufficient control to make him B's employer.

However, if the exercise of control is much more diffuse, such that the person doing the work is not told how to do it, the contract is one for services and the relationship is between what is confusingly known in legal terminology as 'the principal party' and 'an independent contractor'. Obviously, this test is crude and there are borderline cases, but the status of the NHS GP principal as an independent contractor to the health authority has not been seriously questioned in the past.

GPs working as independent contractors should not be told by the health authority how to conduct their day-to-day practice. Health authorities should seek to persuade and advise, not direct or control. British general practice has been strongly influenced by its independent contractor status, which was vigorously upheld at the inception of the NHS in 1948. While hospital doctors became salaried employees of the new service, GPs demanded a greater degree of independence. The remuneration system and the organisation of most practices into partnerships, together with the medico-political institutions which enable GPs to exercise professional self-government, have all been influenced by the independent contractor status.

As independent contractors GP principals are able to exercise considerable discretion and freedom in how they run their practices. However, this autonomy carries with it administrative and financial responsibility for running the business itself, and also responsibility for the clinical services provided. These responsibilities include arranging the provision of adequate premises, staff and equipment. If GPs were employees (like hospital consultants), an NHS trust or health authority would be responsible for providing these resources.

The main advantages of a service operated by independent contractors have been its flexibility and adaptability, and its capacity to offer a more personalised model of care. It also provides opportunities for innovation and diversity without interference, and gives patients the scope for choice between different types of practice. Disadvantages arise if the standards of service are allowed to vary too widely. Those who are responsible for administering GP services sometimes see the independent contractor arrangement as untidy and unsatisfactory, mainly because it lacks the same means of control available to an employer.

No other occupation (apart from the other NHS contractor professions – dentists, chemists and opticians) has enjoyed such a unique partnership with the state, or with the public. General practice has been said to be the original example of the public sector (NHS) and private sector (GPs) operating together to deliver a state service. GPs in other Western developed economies, together with most other professionals, such as dentists, lawyers, architects, surveyors and accountants, are also independent contractors.

In Britain, GPs have jealously guarded their right to practice as independent contractors ever since Lloyd George's national insurance scheme was introduced in 1913. Although the profession supported the idea of a state-funded medical scheme, it was adamantly opposed to employment within a salaried service; it felt that the loss of independent contractor status would undermine the freedom to practise without undue state interference and ultimately put patient care at risk. GPs have always feared that government will seek to direct them in their day-to-day treatment of patients as a way of controlling costs.

Independent contractor status is not without controls though. The terms of service under which GP principals contract with health authorities impose very many requirements and obligations. The implementation of new terms of service in 1990 considerably changed the relationship between individual GPs and health authorities. New controls were introduced over the work of GPs requiring them to submit an annual report to the health authority giving information on their practice arrangements, and to provide a detailed statement of the hours during which they are available to patients for surgery consultations, clinics and home visits.

Additionally, the 1990 contract identified more precisely within the terms of service the services all GPs are required to provide for patients, the procedures that should be undertaken and which patients should be offered which services. For example, the terms of service were amended to make clear that health promotion and illness prevention fall within the remit of general medical services. Since 1990, the terms of service have continued to develop. New requirements introduced since then include the obligation to operate a practice-based complaints procedure, a requirement to monitor the standard of out-of-hours cover provided by commercial or cooperative deputising services and an obligation to purchase an appropriate level of medical defence cover or indemnity insurance.

It is perhaps not surprising, therefore, that the view has gained ground – particularly among younger doctors – that there should be an option for GPs to work as salaried employees within the NHS. Salaried status is often seen as a less open-ended commitment than the independent contractor status and more in keeping with flexible patterns of employment.

Primary Care Act pilot schemes

In 1998, it became possible for the NHS to contract with a new type of provider of GP services. These providers are known as Primary Care Act pilot schemes and, for the first time, do not require the health authority to hold a contract with an individual GP principal.

Instead, the health authority can enter into a contract the detail of which is negotiated with the pilot scheme provider. This could be a GP partnership, an NHS trust, a group of nurses or some other body made up of what are identified as 'members of the NHS family'. The pilot scheme provider is responsible for ensuring that sufficient GPs are engaged to deliver services to patients.

Pilot scheme providers are, like GP principals, contractors to the NHS and thus able to determine, within the constraints of the contract negotiated with the health authority, the arrangements for providing services to patients. Health authorities are required to ensure that all contracts with pilot scheme providers ensure the delivery of services at least equivalent to those provided by GP principals. GPs engaged by pilot schemes to provide patient services can work as salaried employees of the scheme, as contractors to the scheme or as partners or shareholders in the scheme itself.

These new arrangements are experimental and the pilot schemes will be reviewed in 2001; those judged to be successful may be made into permanent arrangements.

Non-principals

There is a wide variety of options for doctors wishing to work in general practice without becoming a GP principal.

GP principals and pilot scheme providers are all able to engage GPs to work for them as locums and as salaried employees (sometimes called assistants), subject to health authority approval. In addition, some GP principals are able to employ an associate GP. There are also opportunities to work for GP deputising services and out-of-hours cooperatives.

GPs who have been out of practice for some time or who wish to maintain their skills during an absence from practice are able to work under the doctors' retainer scheme with a limited sessional commitment.

2 How GPs' pay is determined

The Doctors' and Dentists' Review Body (DDRB) was set up in 1960 as a consequence of the recommendations of a Royal Commission known as the Pilkington Commission. It recommends to the government remuneration levels for doctors (and dentists) working in the NHS.

The Pilkington Commission was concerned with ensuring that doctors' pay should not be used to regulate pay movements in the wider economy and wanted to see it removed from the political arena. The Commission considered various options, including direct negotiations, collective bargaining through Whitley machinery (used by most health service employees to negotiate pay and conditions of service) and arbitration. It finally recommended an independent review body and laid down its ground rules (*see* Box 2.1).

How the Review Body system works

Although the Review Body is prepared to receive evidence from any interested party, it concentrates on evidence from a few key sources (*see* Box 2.2). Both sides, the professions and the Health Departments, normally submit written evidence to the Review Body on the same day, and also exchange their evidence. This means that each side prepares its case 'in the dark' without seeing the other's evidence. The BMA's evidence is usually published shortly after submission.

The next stage involves oral hearings. The Review Body meets each side to clarify the written evidence and discuss other points of concern. The parties also use the oral sessions to emphasise or update any matter in their written evidence.

Having considered the evidence, the Review Body reports in confidence to the Prime Minister and Secretaries of State responsible for health. Further

Box 2.1: The Review Body's ground rules as laid down by the Pilkington Commission

- the Review Body's main task was to exercise 'good judgement'

- although the government had the ultimate power to decide, Review Body recommendations must only be rejected by government very rarely, and for most obviously compelling reasons

- government should deal with Review Body recommendations promptly

- the remuneration of doctors should be determined primarily, though not exclusively, by external comparison with other professions and similarly qualified employees

- doctors should not be used by governments as part of their machinery for regulating the economy; they have a right to be treated fairly and the profession should assist the Review Body by willingly providing information about earnings

- doctors' earnings should not be determined according to short-term supply and demand considerations

Box 2.2: Main sources of evidence to the Review Body

- written evidence from the medical profession prepared by the BMA

- written evidence from the dental profession

- written evidence from the Health Departments

- joint written evidence agreed between the profession and the Health Departments, usually dealing with matters agreed in negotiation

- jointly agreed statistical information, e.g. evidence on GP principals' earnings and expenses

- independent evidence prepared or commissioned by the Review Body's secretariat (Office of Manpower Economics), e.g. surveys conducted at the request of the Review Body time elapses before the report is published and the government announces its decision on whether to implement the recommendations (usually in February of each year).

Since its establishment the Review Body's terms of reference have been amended, following negotiations between the parties. The most recent change was in 1998, when the government sought to impose a requirement that the Review Body take explicit account of affordability in its recommendations on doctors' pay. The BMA resisted this change and eventually negotiated a compromise that would ensure equal weight was given to the evidence submitted by both parties on this issue. The current terms of reference are shown in Box 2.3.

Box 2.3: Doctors' and Dentists' Review Body: current terms of reference

The Review Body on doctors' and dentists' remuneration is independent. Its role is to make recommendations to the Prime Minister, the Secretary of State for Health, the Secretary of State for Scotland and the Secretary of State for Wales on the remuneration of doctors and dentists taking any part in the NHS.

In reaching its recommendations, the Review Body is to have regard to the following considerations:

• the need to recruit, retain and motivate doctors and dentists

• the Health Departments' output targets for the delivery of services, as set out by the government

• the funds available to the Health Departments as set out in the government's Departmental Expenditure Limits

• the government's inflation target.

The Review Body is also required to take careful account of the economic and other evidence submitted by the government, staff and professional representatives, and others.

Reports and recommendations should be submitted jointly to the Secretary of State for Health, the Secretary of State for Scotland, the Secretary of State for Wales and the Prime Minister.

GP principals' remuneration

As independent contractors, GP principals are paid a gross income by the NHS, out of which they meet their practice expenses, including staff salaries, the cost of premises, and motoring expenses. The payment system for these doctors is based on a principle known as 'cost plus'; payments received are intended to both cover expenses and provide a net income (before tax).

The Review Body recommends what it considers to be an appropriate level of net income for GP principals and, taking account of this recommendation, the government then decides on the average level of income for all GP principals in any year. In fact, individual GP principals receive greatly varying amounts depending on the particular circumstances of their practices; expenses and list sizes differ and GPs provide a varying range of services. Virtually all earn either more or less than the average; it is exceptionally rare to find a GP principal whose earnings coincide exactly with the average intended figure.

The component for expenses is added to net income. All expenses incurred in providing general medical services are paid back to the profession in full: some are paid directly to the individual GP principal who actually incurs them (these are known as directly reimbursed expenses); the remainder is reimbursed indirectly on an averaging basis through the fees and allowances. Thus, the exact amount an individual GP principal receives in indirectly reimbursed expenses will not, except by pure chance, equal their expenditure, and in practice, there will be a strong incentive for each principal to economise on his or her own practice expenses.

Although this way of dealing with expenses is complex and can lead to anomalies and inequalities, it does recognise the independent contractor status of GP principals, which is fundamentally different from that of salaried doctors employed elsewhere in the NHS. A possible alternative approach could have been to require each GP principal to submit to the health authority a monthly or quarterly claim for expenses, which it would check (and no doubt query on occasion). If this arrangement were adopted, GP principals would reduce their independence to choose how to run their practices. The significance of this is not always recognised by those who call for increased direct reimbursement.

It has been argued that because, on average, a third of any practice's expenses are repaid indirectly through the fees and allowances, irrespective of what it actually spends, the less an individual practice spends the greater will be its profits. Although there is some truth in this view, it does not represent the whole picture. GP principals are directly reimbursed the cost of providing many of the most costly items (for example, surgery premises and practice staff). A GP principal who chooses to underfund his or her practice will find it lagging behind neighbouring practices. A contrary, more positive, view is that if those GP principals who are unwilling to invest in their own practices overcame their reticence, the profession as a whole would benefit through the indirect reimbursement system and general practice would become more capital intensive. For example, if every GP principal decided to invest in an ECG machine, under the present system the NHS would have no option but to fund this investment through the indirect reimbursement scheme.

An explanation of how GP principals' expenditure on defence body subscriptions is indirectly reimbursed illustrates this point. Every GP principal is now required to subscribe to a medical defence body or to arrange indemnity insurance. The amount each is required to pay is therefore broadly similar. These subscriptions have been paid by most GP principals ever since the present remuneration structure was established in the 1960s and this expenditure is therefore built into the system. The Review Body is aware that defence body subscriptions must now be paid by all GP principals and that these have increased substantially. It is consequently able to make provision for this expenditure in its estimate of expenses, including an element to take account of anticipated increases in the subscription rate. As all GP principals are required to pay such a subscription, it is important that reimbursement through fees and allowances is as close to the prevailing rates as possible, with future increases taken into account.

Fully and directly reimbursed expenditure

Certain practice expenses are reimbursed directly to each GP principal. However, while the direct reimbursement is treated as practice income, the expenditure is claimed against income tax. The GP principal's tax returns can therefore be used to calculate those expenses that need to be reimbursed indirectly through the fees and allowances. Direct reimbursements may be full or partial. Those items reimbursed directly in full are listed in Box 2.4.

Full direct reimbursement of all spending under any heading occurs only when the government or some public agency has direct control over its costs, as is the case with national insurance contributions. Likewise, GP principals receive full direct reimbursement of surgery rent if the rent is approved by a district valuer. A GP trainer receives full reimbursement of the registrar's salary and car allowance, and employer's national insurance

---

Box 2.4: Items of GP expenditure that are reimbursed directly in full

- surgery rent and uniform business rate, water rates, water meter installation and charges, and refuse collection charges
- employer's national insurance contributions in respect of GP registrars and some practice staff
- employer's pension contributions in respect of GP registrars and some practice staff
- net ingredient cost plus VAT of drugs dispensed under the drug tariff

---

and superannuation contributions, again because all these costs are within the control of government.

Expenditure that is directly reimbursed in part

The most common partial direct reimbursement is the refund of practice staff salaries. The imposition of cash limits on health authority funding for direct reimbursement has meant that the percentage of staff salaries refunded may vary. Health authorities have discretion to determine the level of direct reimbursement and thus it may vary from zero to 100%. In England and Wales, primary care groups and local health groups are expected to advise health authorities on the level of reimbursement practices should receive.

A scheme for the partial direct reimbursement of computing costs introduced in 1990 has provided for the direct payment of a proportion of the costs of purchasing, leasing, upgrading and maintaining a computer system. More recently, the out-of-hours development fund has provided for the partial reimbursement of the costs associated with maintaining or improving high standard out-of-hours care.

Indirectly reimbursed expenditure

Each year the Review Body uses a sample survey of GP principals' tax returns to estimate how much GPs as a whole spend on providing general medical services. By taking into account the total amount of health authority expenditure on direct reimbursements, it calculates an average figure to meet the necessary indirect reimbursement of expenses. This figure for average indirect expenses is added to the level of pre-tax pay which the Review Body considers appropriate for GP principals to earn, known as intended average net remuneration (IANR), and the resulting figure is called intended average gross remuneration (IAGR). The various fees and allowances that comprise a GP principal's pay are then adjusted, subject to any government decision on pay, so that during the year they yield, for the notional average GP principal, the total gross remuneration which the Review Body has deemed appropriate.

This exercise is complex and because the 'targets' set by the Review Body are not always met, any under- or over-payment is allowed for in subsequent years. Because the Health Department is appraised of how much has been paid to GP principals after the end of every financial year, it is not difficult to compare the level of average gross pay received with the Review Body's original target. Average net pay is more difficult to calculate because it depends on an analysis of income tax returns.

Because GP principals wish to obtain tax relief, they tell the Inland Revenue how much expenditure they have incurred in providing general medical services. This is the key source of information for estimating GP principals' overall expenses. Once a year, the Inland Revenue provides anonymised information relating to a sample of tax returns, which include professional and partnership expenses.

GP accounts

As the level of expenses to be reimbursed is always based on an examination of a sample of income tax returns, it is vital that all GP principals record all their expenses correctly.

For revenue items, the full amounts of both directly and indirectly reimbursed expenses should be entered, including those items that may not appear in cash books, bank statements or cheque books. Examples include those payments made by health authorities directly to local authorities or other bodies on behalf of the practice, such as health centre rents, waste disposal charges and levies. The practice of 'netting off' expenses against matching income must be avoided; failure to include expenses, however small, has the potential to reduce the funding available to the profession as a whole. In particular, practices should take note to include their expenditure on out-of-hours services, including any amounts paid on their behalf by health authorities.

Where capital items are concerned – for example, computers and equip-ment purchased from incentive scheme savings – standard accounting practice should be followed. This will usually involve depreciating assets net of any reimbursement received.

Non-principals' remuneration

The Review Body does not play a direct part in setting the remuneration of most non-principal GPs. It does, however, recommend a salary scale for doctors engaged as GP associates and has undertaken to monitor the re-muneration of non-principals engaged in Primary Care Act pilot schemes.

For most non-principals, therefore, their remuneration will be a matter for negotiation with the practice for whom they work. The BMA can advise on suggested rates, which are set in the light of the Review Body's recommendations for GP principals' remuneration.

3 GPs' terms of service

Where to obtain advice and assistance

BMA members should contact their local BMA office for expert advice and assistance. Help can also be obtained from health authority and LMC offices. The BMA web site is at www.bma.org.uk

Further reading includes Ellis N and Chisholm J (1997) *Making Sense of the Red Book* (3e). Radcliffe Medical Press, Oxford, the Red Book itself and the NHS (General Medical Services) Regulations 1992 (as amended).

GP principals working in the NHS have a contract with the health authority to provide general medical services for their NHS patients. It is important to note that the contract is with the health authority not the patient, in contrast to most other countries where doctors have a direct contractual commitment to patients. Given this independent contractor status with a statutory authority in a publicly funded health service, it is not surprising that the contract has been enshrined in legislation, the NHS (General Medical Services) Regulations (*see* Box 3.1). Separate regulations (the Directions to Health Authorities Concerning the Implementation of Pilot Schemes – Personal Medical Service) set the framework within which Primary Care Act pilot schemes operate. These require that pilot scheme doctors provide services equivalent to those provided by GP principals.

The NHS (General Medical Services) Regulations, which include in Schedule 2 the terms of service, provide the legal framework within which GP principals work. Because these regulations are laid down by Parliament, their style is legalistic, making them difficult for a layman to comprehend; a difficulty which is compounded by subsequent amending legislation. The

---

Box 3.1: National Health Service (General Medical Services) Regulations 1992

The regulations are in seven parts

I   General: citation and commencement; interpretation; scope and terms of service

II   The Medical List: medical list; applying for inclusion or succession to a vacancy; amending of or withdrawing from it; removal from it; local directory of family doctors

III Medical Practices Committee: membership; reports; procedure for filling vacancies; certifying sale of goodwill not involved

IV   General Medical Services other than Child Health Surveillance Services, Contraceptive Services, Maternity Medical Services and Minor Surgery Services: describes how patients apply to be on a doctor's list; how patients are assigned to doctors; the limits on list size; how patients transfer to another doctor; how patients are removed from a doctor's list; arrangements for temporary residents; temporary arrangements for running a practice

V   Child Health Surveillance Services, Contraceptive Services, Maternity Medical Services and Minor Surgery Services: explains the separate lists for each of these services and how these services are obtained

VI   Payments to doctors: requires the Secretary of State to publish the Statement of Fees and Allowances (the Red Book) and to pay doctors accordingly

VII Miscellaneous: whether a substance is a drug; appointment of medical advisers; guidance to doctors

---

regulations have been amended on many occasions; more than a dozen amendments were enacted after 1 April 1985 following the introduction of the limited list of NHS drugs. In November 1989, major amendments were introduced to implement new contractual arrangements with effect from 1 April 1990, and each GP principal was sent a copy of the amended terms of service. In April 1992, a completely revised and consolidated version of the regulations was made, and a copy of this was also sent to each GP principal. In England and Wales, this new version rationalised the arrangement of the regulations and no longer included the pharmaceutical services regulations. Therefore, at the same time as the consolidated general medical services regulations were published, consolidated pharmaceutical services regulations were also distributed. They include regulations governing the provision of pharmaceutical services by doctors and how rurality is determined in relation to doctor and chemist dispensing. Since 1992 the regulations have been amended on a further 16 occasions and, as the NHS continues to develop, further changes can always be expected. There are equivalent regulations in Scotland.

There is an understandable reluctance to provide a definitive explanatory guide to the regulations. Since they carry the force of law, any dispute about their application or meaning can be resolved only by reference to the original text. Each copy of the regulations, and subsequent amending regulations, is accompanied by an official explanatory note, but it is always stated that this note does not form part of the regulations as such. Nevertheless, a doctor needs to know what is required to fulfil his or her contract with the health authority. In part, this knowledge is acquired from colleagues and partners, and the health authority. Advice from both LMCs and BMA local offices helps to familiarise doctors with the regulations and the terms of service, and make them aware of current issues concerning their interpretation and application.

It is essential that all GPs are aware of the regulations because they contain the terms of service which form the basis of their NHS contract. Every GP principal should have access to a copy of the 1992 regulations and amending regulations. Copies are distributed by health authorities and additional copies may be obtained from them. Nevertheless, many practices rarely refer to the regulations, and if a difficulty arises they usually seek advice from their LMC or health authority. The regulations should be referred to if problems arise, and if there is any doubt abut their meaning GPs should seek advice from their LMC or BMA office. A separate set of regulations deals with alleged breaches of the terms of service by a GP principal. These are normally dealt with by the disciplinary committee of a neighbouring health authority, the NHS (Service Committees and Tribunal) Regulations 1992. The health authority with which the GP is in contract is a party to the disciplinary proceeding, so its own disciplinary committee cannot conduct the hearing.

The commentary below focuses on the main aspects of the terms of service; it should help GP principals to understand that part of the regulations (an appendix entitled Schedule 2) which contains these terms of service. **This selective commentary is not a substitute for the original text and should not be quoted if any problem arises.**

The terms of service for GP principals

Professional judgement

When a GP has to decide what, if any, professional action needs to be taken under the terms of service, he or she is not expected to exercise a higher degree of skill, knowledge and care than may reasonably be expected of GPs generally. Any GP who wants clarification on a matter involving professional judgement should consult his or her LMC or medical defence body, or the GMC publication *Good Medical Practice*. The same principle also applies to GPs providing child health surveillance, maternity medical services or minor surgery services; in each case the level of skill, knowledge and care expected is that which may reasonably be expected of any doctor included in the appropriate list.

Patients

The terms of service specify those categories of persons who are a GP principal's patients (*see* Box 3.2). Most are self-evident. However, it is important to note that if a patient seeking treatment claims to be on a doctor's list but fails to produce a medical card, and the doctor has reasonable doubts about the claim, treatment should nevertheless be provided and a fee may be claimed. If the patient is subsequently able to prove to the health authority that he or she is on the doctor's list, the fee has to be refunded. In practice, few practices levy this charge; it is likely to be misunderstood and is rarely worthwhile.

Providing child health surveillance and minor surgery

GPs on the relevant health authority list may provide to a patient on their list (or on a partner's list or the list of a GP with whom they are in group practice) child health surveillance and/or minor surgery services, and be paid for these services.

A GP who has agreed to provide child health surveillance services should:

- provide those services listed in Box 3.3 (except for any examination the parent refuses to allow) until the child attains the age of five years
- maintain the records specified in Box 3.4
- provide the health authority with the information specified in Box 3.5.

Box 3.2: Who are a GP principal's patients?

The main categories are:

- persons on the GP's list
- persons whom the GP has accepted or agreed to accept on the list whether or not the health authority has received notification of that acceptance
- for a limited period of up to 14 days, persons the GP has refused to accept on to the list, if they live in the practice area and are not on the list of another doctor in the same area, or persons the GP has refused to accept as temporary residents
- persons who have been assigned to the GP under Regulation 21
- for a limited period, persons about whom the GP has been notified that an application has been made for assignment to him or her
- persons accepted as temporary residents
- persons eligible for acceptance as temporary residents whom the GP agrees to take a cervical smear from, vaccinate or immunise
- persons to whom the GP is requested to give treatment which is immediately required owing to an accident or other emergency at any place in the practice area, or any persons to whom the GP agrees on request to give treatment which is immediately required owing to an accident or other emergency at any place in the health authority locality, provided that there is no other doctor at the time otherwise obliged and available to give treatment
- persons for whom the GP is acting as a deputy to another doctor under the terms of service
- persons whom the GP has been appointed to treat temporarily
- persons for whom the GP has undertaken to provide child health surveillance or minor surgery services
- women for whom the GP has undertaken to provide contraceptive or maternity medical services
- persons whose own doctor has been relieved of responsibility for them during hours arranged with the health authority, for whom the GP has accepted responsibility during those hours.

Box 3.3: Child health surveillance: services

These services comprise:

- the monitoring:

    (a) by the consideration of information concerning the child received by or on behalf of the doctor, and

    (b) on any occasion when the child is examined or observed by or on behalf of the doctor (whether pursuant to subparagraph (b) or otherwise) of the health, well being, and physical, mental and social development (all of which characteristics are referred to as 'development') of the child while under the age of five years with a view to detecting any deviations from normal development

- the examination of the child by or on behalf of the doctor on so many occasions and at such intervals as shall have been agreed by the health authority in whose district the child resides ('the relevant health authority') for the purpose of the provision of child health surveillance services generally in that district.

Box 3.4: Child health surveillance: records

The GP should keep an accurate record of:

- development of the child under the age of five years, compiled as soon as is reasonably practicable following the first examination and, where appropriate, amended following each subsequent examination, and

- the responses (if any) to offers made to the child's parent for the child to undergo any examination.

GPs who have agreed to provide minor surgery services should:

- offer to provide any of the procedures listed in Box 3.6 as appropriate

- if providing minor surgery services to a patient not on their list, inform the patient's GP in writing of the outcome of the procedure.

Box 3.5: Child health surveillance: information

The GP should provide the health authority with the following information:

- a statement, to be prepared and dispatched to the relevant health authority as soon as is reasonably practicable following any examination, of the procedures undertaken in the course of that examination and of the doctor's findings in relation to each such procedure
- such further information regarding the development of the child while under the age of five years as the relevant health authority may request.

Box 3.6: Minor surgery procedures

Injections	intra-articular
	peri-articular
	varicose veins
	haemorrhoids
Aspirations	joints
	cysts
	bursae
	hydrocele
Incisions	abscesses
	cysts
	thrombosed piles
Excisions	sebaceous cysts
	lipoma
	skin lesions for histology
	intradermal naevi, papillomata, dermatofibromata and similar conditions
	warts
	removal of toenails (partial or complete)
Curette cautery and cryocautery	warts and verrucae other skin lesions (e.g. molluscum contagiosum)
Other	removal of foreign bodies
	nasal cautery

Terminating responsibility for patients

GP principals may apply to the health authority to have a patient removed from their list. This takes effect on the day when the patient is accepted by, or assigned to, another doctor, or on the eighth day after the application, whichever is sooner. However, if the GP is treating the person when removal would normally take effect, the health authority should be informed and removal will take effect only on the eighth day after it receives notification that the patient no longer requires treatment, or upon acceptance by another doctor, whichever occurs first.

The terms of service do not require that GPs give patients any explanation of the reason for removal from the list. However, the BMA's strong advice to doctors is that they should always consider any breakdown in the doctor–patient relationship very carefully and removing a patient from the list should always be a last resort. Where this happens GPs should, as a matter of good practice, usually offer the patient an explanation.

Since April 1994, doctors have been able to require the health authority to remove immediately from their list any patient who has given them reasonable cause to fear for their safety, including those who have shown threatening behaviour. The criterion is the GP's reasonable fear. Before immediate removal, the GP *must* inform the police of the incident. This is, in any case, good practice, since a criminal offence under the Public Order or Offences Against the Person Acts will usually have been committed. Having registered the incident with the police, GPs should notify the health authority of their wish to remove the patient; regardless of whether its offices are open at the time, the removal takes effect from the moment the message reaches the authority. Fax or telephone notification is sufficient, but this should be confirmed in writing. GPs are also required to notify the patient, but this can be done by post, or via the police, as appropriate.

The right to remove a patient has to be set out against the duty of the health authority to assign a patient to a GP if the patient is not acceptable on a voluntary basis. In an area served by only one GP this can severely limit a doctor's right to remove a patient.

A GP may agree with a patient to stop providing her with maternity medical services and, failing agreement, may apply for permission to terminate the arrangement. The health authority may agree to this after considering the views of either party and consulting the LMC. If the GP stops providing maternity medical services the patient must be told so that she can make alternative arrangements.

A GP's agreement to provide child health surveillance services may be terminated:

- by either parent or doctor

- if the child has been removed from the doctor's list (or his or her partner's list or that of a doctor with whom he or she is associated in a group practice)
- if the parent fails to respond within 42 days to an invitation to arrange for the child to attend for examination.

Again, the GP should inform the health authority and, where appropriate, the patient, if he or she no longer intends to provide these services.

Services to patients

The terms of service require GPs to provide their patients with all necessary and appropriate personal medical services of the type usually provided by GPs. These should be provided at the practice premises or, if the condition of the patient requires, where the patient was living when accepted as a patient, or elsewhere in the practice area. The GP is not required to visit or treat the patient at any other place, but care has to be taken to ensure that neither the GP nor a member of his or her staff implies there is a willingness to visit at an address outside the practice area. If this should happen, the GP may be bound by a duty to visit.

There is no obligation to provide contraceptive services, child health surveillance services, minor surgery services or, except in an emergency, maternity medical services, unless the GP has previously agreed to do so.

The doctor should, unless prevented by an emergency, attend and treat any patient who comes for treatment at the places and during the hours approved by the health authority, other than a patient who attends when an appointment system is in operation and has not made an appointment. In these circumstances the doctor may decline to see the patient during that surgery period, providing the patient's health would not be put at risk and the patient is offered an appointment to attend within a reasonable time. GPs should take all reasonable steps to ensure that a consultation is not so deferred without their knowledge. The regulations specify in detail certain services a GP is required to provide. These include:

- giving advice, as appropriate, to a patient about the patient's general health, and in particular about diet, exercise, the use of tobacco, the consumption of alcohol, and the misuse of drugs and solvents
- offering patients consultations and, where appropriate, physical examinations to identify or reduce the risk of disease or injury
- offering patients, as appropriate, vaccination or immunisation against measles, mumps, rubella, pertussis, poliomyelitis, diphtheria and tetanus
- arranging for patients to be referred to other NHS services

- giving advice to enable patients to obtain help from the local authority social services department.

Paragraph 13 of the terms of service was amended in February 1995 to secure greater flexibility for GPs as to how they may best meet their responsibilities out of hours. The amendment emphasises that GPs themselves are responsible for judging whether or not a consultation is required out of hours, on the basis of the information made available to them about the patient, and allows them similar flexibility when deciding what would be the appropriate location for the consultation, whether it is provided by telephone, at the surgery (or some other clinical setting) or at the patient's home, or whether it requires a direct referral to hospital.

Newly registered patients

If a patient has been accepted on to a GP's list (or assigned to it) the patient should be offered a consultation within 28 days to:

- obtain details of the patient's medical history, and when relevant that of his or her family, relating to:
  - illnesses, immunisations, allergies, hereditary conditions, medication and tests carried out for breast or cervical cancer
  - social factors (including employment, housing and family circumstances) which may affect health
  - lifestyle factors (including diet, exercise, use of tobacco, consumption of alcohol, and misuse of drugs and solvents) which may affect health
  - the current state of the patient's health
- physically examine the patient:
  - measuring height, weight and blood pressure
  - taking and analysing a urine sample to identify the presence of albumin and glucose
- record in the patient's notes the results of this examination
- assess whether and to what extent personal medical services should be provided to the patient
- offer to discuss with the patient (or the parent of a child patient) the conclusions of the consultation as to the state of the patient's health.

When offering a consultation for this purpose, the GP should:

- provide a written invitation – or if the initial invitation is made orally, provide written confirmation
- record in the patient's medical records the date of each invitation and whether it was accepted

- where, as a result of making the invitation, the doctor becomes aware that a patient is no longer residing at the address given in the records, inform the health authority.

A GP is not required to offer a consultation to a newly registered patient if:

- he or she is a restricted services principal (i.e. a principal who has undertaken to provide only child health services, contraceptive services, maternity medical services or minor surgery services, or some combination of these)
- the patient is a child under the age of five years
- the patient was, immediately before joining the list, on that of a partner and had already had a consultation of this kind during the previous 12 months.

If a GP assumes responsibility for a list of patients by taking on a vacant practice, or becomes responsible for a sizeable number of new patients over a short period, they can ask the health authority to defer the obligation to offer these consultations.

Patients not seen within three years

If requested to do so, a GP is required to provide to a patient on his or her list a consultation to assess whether personal medical services are needed, if the patient:

- is between the ages of 16 and 75 years
- has within the preceding three years not attended either a consultation with nor a clinic provided by any doctor in the course of the provision of general medical services.

During this consultation the GP should obtain the information listed in Box 3.7 and offer a physical examination including the procedures listed in Box 3.7. The GP should record the findings and assess whether the patient requires treatment.

Patients aged 75 years and over

Patients over 75 should be offered an annual consultation and a domiciliary visit (which may be combined) to assess whether any treatment is required. This offer should be made within 12 months of the patient's 75th birthday. Similarly if a patient joins a GP's list and is already aged 75 years, the offer should be made within 12 months. The GP should make the offer in writing (or confirm it in writing if made orally) and keep a record of the date of the invitation and whether it was accepted.

Box 3.7: Patients not seen within three years: information to be obtained and procedures to be undertaken during the consultation

Where appropriate the GP should obtain from the patient the following details of his or her medical history and, if relevant to the patient's medical history, that of his or her consanguineous family:

(i)   illnesses, immunisations, allergies, hereditary diseases, medication and tests carried out for breast or cervical cancer

(ii) social factors (including employment, housing and family circumstances) which may affect health

(iii) lifestyle factors (including diet, exercise, use of tobacco, consumption of alcohol, and misuse of drugs or solvents) which may affect health, and

(iv) the current state of the patient's health.

The GP should also offer to undertake a physical examination of the patient, comprising:

(i)   the measurement of blood pressure

(ii) the taking of a urine sample and its analysis to identify the presence of albumin and glucose, and

(iii) the measurements necessary to detect any changes in body mass.

The GP should record in the patient's medical records, the findings arising out of the details supplied by, and any examination of, the patient.

The doctor should also record the findings of the consultation and offer to discuss with the patient any conclusions that have been drawn.

Absences, deputies, assistants and partners

Normally, GP principals should give treatment personally. However, in the case of general medical services, other than maternity medical services, child health surveillance and minor surgery services, the GP is under no obligation to do so and, provided reasonable steps are taken to ensure continuity of care, treatment may be provided by another doctor acting as a deputy, irrespective of whether that doctor is a partner or an assistant.

In addition, it is possible to delegate clinical treatment to a person whom the GP has authorised and who is competent to carry it out (e.g. a qualified nurse).

A doctor on the obstetric list should not, without the health authority's consent, employ a deputy or assistant to provide maternity services who is not (or is not qualified by experience to be) included on the obstetric list, except in an obstetric emergency.

As for child health surveillance services, a GP who has agreed to provide these may employ a deputy or an assistant on a child health surveillance list, or with the health authority's agreement another deputy or assistant. A GP who has agreed to provide minor surgery services may employ a deputy or assistant who is on a minor surgery list.

In general, GP principals are responsible for the acts and omissions of all doctors acting as their deputies, whether the deputy is a partner or an assistant. They are similarly responsible for any person they employ or who acts on their behalf. *However, a GP is not responsible under the terms of service for the acts and omissions of a deputy who is on the medical list of the same or some other health authority.*

The health authority should be informed of any standing deputising arrangements unless the deputy is the GP's assistant or is already on its medical list and carries out these arrangements at the premises where the doctor normally practises. If a GP is absent for more than a week, the health authority should be told who is responsible for the practice during his or her absence.

Before entering into any arrangement with a deputising service, GPs should obtain the health authority's consent. When giving consent, it may impose conditions to ensure that the arrangements are adequate, but must consult the LMC before refusing consent or imposing conditions. The health authority is required to review any consent given or conditions imposed in consultation with the LMC, and may withdraw consent or alter the conditions. A GP may appeal to the Secretary of State against a refusal or withdrawal of consent, or the imposition or variation of conditions.

GPs should take reasonable steps to satisfy themselves that any doctor employed as a deputy or assistant is not disqualified from inclusion on the health authority's list.

Any doctor engaged as a deputy or assistant must be vocationally trained and GPs must take reasonable steps to ensure that they are. The GP should tell the health authority the name of any assistant employed and when this employment ends. A doctor should not employ one or more assistants for more than three months in a period of 12 months without the health authority's consent, but before refusing or withdrawing consent, it must

---

Box 3.8: Transfer of out-of-hours responsibility

An extra paragraph (18A) was added to the terms of service in April 1996 to allow GPs to transfer their out-of-hours responsibility, fully or in part, to another GP on a health authority list. GPs must apply to their health authority for approval for such a transfer of responsibility. Health authorities should only withhold approval in exceptional circumstances and after consulting the LMC. Paragraph 18A(7) sets out the information which GPs should include in their applications.

---

consult the LMC. (A GP may appeal to the Medical Practices Committee (MPC) against refusal or withdrawal of consent.) If consent is withdrawn, the decision will not take effect for a month; but if an appeal is made to the MPC against withdrawal and it dismisses the appeal, the withdrawal takes effect from a date determined by the MPC, not less than one month after the date of dismissal. (A doctor acting as a deputy can treat patients at places and times other than those arranged by the GP for whom he or she is deputising, although regard must be given to the convenience of the patients.)

Arrangements at practice premises

GP principals must provide adequate accommodation at the practice premises having regard to the practice's circumstances or any other premises at which the health authority has agreed they may treat patients, and are required, on receiving a written request from the health authority, to allow the premises to be visited at any reasonable time by a representative of either the health authority or LMC, or both.

If a GP intends to run an appointment system (or succeeds to or joins a practice where one is already running), the health authority should be told about the proposed system or of any proposal to discontinue it.

With certain important exceptions, a GP should not, without the consent of the health authority (or, on appeal, the MPC), start to practise in any premises within one year of their having ceased to be occupied or used for practice purposes by another doctor who within one month of such cessation begins practising at a group practice premises, as a member of a group, or at a health centre less than three miles away from the original premises. (This does not apply if the former occupant gives written consent for another doctor to use the premises.)

Employees

Before employing any member of staff, the GP should ensure that the person is suitably qualified and competent to carry out the required duties. In particular, the doctor should take account of the employee's academic and vocational qualifications, training and previous experience. The GP should also offer the employee reasonable training opportunities.

Availability to patients

Any GP should normally be available at times and places approved by the health authority and must inform patients of their availability. In general, the health authority will not give approval unless satisfied that the GP is normally available:

- 42 weeks in any period of 12 months
- during not less than 26 hours in any such week
- on five days in any such week
- with hours of availability which are likely to be convenient to patients.

There are important exceptions to this basic requirement:

- a GP may seek to be normally available for 26 hours over a four-day week, if involved in health-related activities other than providing general medical services to his or her patients (*see* Box 3.9 for a broad definition of health-related activities). But the four-day availability will not be approved by the health authority if it considers that the effectiveness of the doctor's services to patients is likely to be significantly reduced or patients are likely to suffer significant inconvenience
- a GP principal may seek to be available for less than 26 hours a week, if practising in a partnership. In this case there are two options:
  - less than 26 hours but not less than 19 hours
  - less than 19 hours but not less than 13 hours
- two doctors in partnership may apply for health authority approval to be jointly available for 26 hours a week.

The NHS Executive has issued important guidance to health authorities on the availability requirements under the terms of service. Strictly speaking, under the regulations the availability in question has to be looked at on the basis of each individual doctor's application in respect of his or her hours and their convenience to patients. The regulations do not require

---

Box 3.9: List of health-related activities

- activities connected with the organisation or training of the medical profession
- activities connected with the provision of medical care or treatment
- activities connected with the improvement of the quality of care or treatment
- activities connected with the administration of general medical services
- appointments concerning medical education or training
- medical appointments within the health service other than in relation to the provision of general medical services
- medical appointments under the Crown, with government departments or agencies, or public or local authorities
- appointments concerning the regulation of the medical profession or service on the MPC
- membership of a primary care group or equivalent
- membership of a medical audit advisory group

---

health authorities to take partners' availability into account, but nor do they preclude them from doing so except in circumstances where:

- this would result in arrangements which were not convenient to the GP's own patients

  OR
- the GP whose application is being considered objects.

The Health Department's view is that, provided these circumstances do not apply, health authorities may take partnership availability into account. Appeals made against their decisions on availability have highlighted several areas of uncertainty. The most common of these are summarised below.

- Health authorities *cannot* stipulate which specific days doctors must be available. Under the regulations it is for doctors to choose which days they wish to be available. The 'convenience to patients' rule then applies to the spread of the hours across the doctor's chosen days. They may not, for example, require a doctor to provide a surgery on a Saturday, if that doctor is already available on five other days each week.

- Many health authorities have agreed local policies as to how they deal with applications by doctors for approval of hours of availability. Nevertheless, each application has to be considered individually against the requirements of the terms of service. They may not hold that a doctor's proposed hours are inconvenient merely because they do not meet local criteria. There must be a recognised procedure for looking at each doctor's individual circumstances and convenience to patients.

- The regulations do not specifically require doctors to work the *same* five days every week. There is therefore no bar on doctors working a rota system, provided that it meets the 'convenience to patients' tests; for example, a fixed and regular rota, which is easily understandable by, and is advertised to, patients.

- Health authorities have the authority, when approving a doctor's hours of availability, to make its approval subject to specified conditions. However, one such condition may *not* be that approval is limited to a certain period (e.g. approving the hours subject to a review in six months). Any conditions laid down must involve an amendment to the proposed hours of availability which, if accepted by the GP, would result in the hours being agreed.

- Health authorities do not have the authority to designate a doctor, who has applied on the basis of full-time availability, as a part-time doctor and to reduce rates of pay accordingly. They may *only* reduce rates of payment to those appropriate for GPs working part time, where it is a condition imposed by the MPC that the doctor should work part time.

- In the case of doctors applying for four-day availability it is not necessary for the 'health-related activities' concerned to be performed on the day for which relief is being sought. Provided these activities are on a fixed and regular basis, a doctor may be entitled to apply for reduced availability on the basis of the cumulative effects of such activities. Recently, it has been made clear to health authorities that service on primary care groups and local health groups should be taken into account in determining hours of availability.

Practice area

A GP principal may not open premises in an area where, at the time of the application, the MPC consider the number of GPs to be adequate. Subject to this condition, a GP may apply at any time to the health authority for consent to alter the practice area. (If it refuses consent, the GP may appeal to the Secretary of State.)

Notification of change of residence

If a GP changes his or her place of residence, the health authority should be told in writing within 28 days.

Records

A GP should keep adequate records of the illnesses and treatment of patients on the forms supplied by the health authority and should send these to it on request as soon as possible. Within 14 days of being informed by the health authority of a patient's death (or not later than one month after otherwise learning of it), a GP should return the records to the health authority. The terms of service do not, at present, provide for the maintenance of electronic patient records without paper copies.

Certification

A GP should issue to patients or their personal representatives free of charge the certificates listed in Box 3.10 if they are reasonably required. However, a GP is not obliged to do so if the patient is being attended by another doctor (other than a partner, assistant or deputy) or is not being treated by, or under the supervision of, a doctor. In certain circumstances, a GP may issue a statement, without an examination, advising the patient to refrain from work for a period of up to a month, provided a written report not more than a month old has been received from another doctor at a hospital, place of employment or other institution. The other doctor should not be a partner, assistant or deputy.

Accepting fees

There are only limited circumstances in which GP principals may accept fees from their NHS patients. GPs must not demand or accept a fee or any other form of remuneration for any treatment, including maternity medical services, whether provided under the terms of service or not, given to a person for whose treatment they are responsible. Doctors must take all practical steps to ensure that any partner, deputy or assistant does not demand or accept any remuneration for treatment given to their patients unless, of course, the partner, deputy or assistant would have been entitled to charge if the patient had been on his or her own list.

There are, however, certain specific circumstances in which a GP may accept a fee. These are listed in Box 3.11.

There are other certificates and reports which are not part of a GP's NHS obligations to patients. Fees for these are a matter to be agreed between

Box 3.10: List of prescribed medical certificates

Purpose of certificate	*Relevant legislation*
1 To claim payment, to prove inability to work or incapacity, and to draw pensions, etc.	Naval and Marine Pay and Pensions Act 1986
	Air Force (Constitution) Act 1917
	Pensions (Navy, Army, Air Force and Mercantile Marine) Act 1939
	Personal Injuries (Emergency Provisions) Act 1939
	Pensions (Mercantile Marine) Act 1942
	Polish Resettlement Act 1947
	Home Guard Act 1951
	Social Security Act 1975
	Industrial Injuries and Diseases (Old Cases) Act 1975
	Parts I and III of the Social Security and Housing Benefits Act 1982
	Parts II and V of, and Schedule 4 to, the Social Security Act 1986
2 To prove pregnancy so as to obtain welfare foods	Section 13 of the Social Security Act (1988)
3 To show fitness for inhaling analgesia in childbirth	Nurses, Midwives and Health Visitors Act 1979
4 To register a stillbirth	Births and Deaths Registration Act 1953
5 To enable payment to be made to an institution or other person in case of mental disorder of persons entitled to payment from public funds	Section 142 of the Mental Health Act 1983

Box 3.10: *continued*

Purpose of certificate	Relevant legislation
6 To prove unfitness for jury service	Juries Act 1974
7 To prove unfitness for medical examination	National Service Act 1948
8 To support late application for reinstatement in civil employment or notification on non-availability, owing to sickness	Reinstatement in Civil Employment Act 1944 Reinstatement in Civil Employment Act 1950 Reserve Forces Act 1980
9 To register as an absent voter on grounds of physical incapacity	Representation of the People Act 1983
10 To support a severely mentally impaired person's claim for exemption from paying the community charge	Local Government Finance Act 1988
11 To support a claim by or on behalf of a severely mentally impaired person for exemption from liability to pay the Council Tax or eligibility for a discount in respect of the amount of Council Tax payable	Local Government Finance Act 1992

the GP and the person or organisation requesting the certificate or report; the BMA suggests fees for these procedures. GPs are also required to provide medical studies for the Benefits Agency, or their agents, certain reports on patients for social security purposes.

A doctor must not demand or accept a fee or other remuneration from a patient for prescribing or supplying any drug or chemical reagent or appliance, unless the patient requires it solely in anticipation of the onset of an ailment outside the UK for which he or she is not currently being treated.

Box 3.11: Specific circumstances in which a GP may accept a fee

- from any statutory body for services rendered for the purpose of that body's statutory functions

- from any body, employer or school for a routine medical examination of persons for whose welfare the body, employer or school is responsible, or an examination of such persons for the purpose of advising the body, employer or school of any administrative action they might take

- for treatment which is not a type usually provided by GPs and which is given:
  - (i) pursuant to the provisions of section 65 of the Act, or
  - (ii) in a registered nursing home which is not providing services under the Act if, in either case, the doctor is serving on the staff of a hospital providing services under the Act as a specialist providing treatment of the kind the patient requires and if, within seven days of giving the treatment, the doctor supplies the health authority, on a form provided by it for the purpose, with such information about the treatment as it may require

- under Section 158 of the Road Traffic Act 1988

- from a dentist in respect of the provision at his or her request of an anaesthetic for a person for whom the dentist is providing general dental services

- when he or she treats a patient under paragraph 4(3), in which case he or she shall be entitled to demand and accept a reasonable fee (recoverable under paragraph 39) for any treatment given, if he or she gives the patient a receipt on a form supplied by the health authority

- for attending and examining (but not otherwise treating) a patient at his or her request at a police station in connection with proceedings which the police are minded to bring against him or her

- for treatment consisting of an immunisation for which no remuneration is payable by the health authority in pursuance of the statement made under regulation 34 and which is requested in connection with travel abroad

Box 3.11: *continued*

- for circumcising a patient for whom such an operation is requested on religious grounds and is not needed on any medical ground

- for prescribing or providing drugs which a patient requires to have in his or her possession solely in anticipation of the onset of an ailment while he or she is outside the UK but for which he or she is not requiring treatment when the medicine is prescribed

- for a medical examination to enable a decision to be made whether or not it is inadvisable on medical grounds for a person to wear a seat belt

- where the person is not one to whom any of paragraphs (a), (b) or (c) of section 38(1) of the Act applies (including by reason of regulations under section 38(6) of that Act), for testing the sight of that person

- where he or she is a doctor who is authorised or required by a health authority under regulation 20 of the pharmaceutical services regulations to provide drugs, medicines or appliances to a patient and provides for that patient, otherwise than under pharmaceutical services, any Scheduled drug

- for prescribing or providing drugs for malaria chemo-prophylaxis

Prescribing and dispensing

A GP is required to supply drugs or listed appliances needed for a patient's immediate treatment before a supply can be obtained elsewhere. In the course of treating a patient under general medical services, a GP must not issue a prescription for a drug or other substance listed in schedule 10 to the regulations (the 'black list') for supply under the NHS. In the case of a drug listed under schedule 11 to the regulations, a doctor may prescribe only in the circumstances specified. A GP may prescribe privately items not available on NHS prescriptions, but may not charge for doing so. The GP can only charge for the item itself if he or she is already entitled to dispense to a patient and the GP can only do so for a particular course of treatment.

Practice leaflets

A GP or partnership should prepare a practice leaflet including the information in Box 3.12. It should be reviewed at least annually for accuracy and an up-to-date copy should be made available to the health authority, each patient on the doctor's list and anyone else who reasonably requires one.

Box 3.12: Information to be included in practice leaflets

Personal and professional details of the doctor:

- full name
- sex
- medical qualifications registered by the General Medical Council
- date and place of first registration as medical practitioner
- the times approved by the health authority during which the doctor is personally available for consultation by his or her patients at his or her practice premises
- whether an appointment system is operated by the doctor for consultations at his or her practice premises
- if there is an appointment system, the method of obtaining a non-urgent appointment and the method of obtaining an urgent appointment
- the method of obtaining a non-urgent domiciliary visit and the method of obtaining an urgent domiciliary visit
- the doctor's arrangements for providing personal medical services when he or she is not personally available
- the name and address of any other doctor with whom the doctor has made an out-of-hours arrangement under paragraph 18(A) of the terms of service; also his or her availability times and contact details
- the method by which patients are to obtain repeat prescriptions from the doctor
- if the doctor's practice is a dispensing practice, the arrangements for dispensing prescriptions
- if the doctor provides clinics for his or her patients, their frequency, duration and purpose

---

Box 3.12: *continued*

- the number of staff, other than doctors, assisting the doctor in his or her practice, and a description of their roles

- whether the doctor provides maternity medical services, contraceptive services, child health surveillance services or minor surgery services

- whether the doctor works single-handed, in partnership, part-time or on a job-sharing basis, or within a group practice

- the nature of any arrangements whereby the doctor or his or her staff receive patients' comments on his or her provision of general medical services

- the geographical boundary of his or her practice area by reference to a sketch, diagram or plan

- whether the doctor's practice premises have suitable access for all disabled patients and, if not, the reasons why they are unsuitable for particular types of disability

- if an assistant is employed, details for him as specified in paragraph 1–5 of this table

- if the practice is either a GP training practice for the purposes of the NHS (Vocational Training) Regulations 1979 or under-takes the teaching of undergraduate medical students, and the nature of arrangements for drawing this to the attention of patients.

Complaints

In April 1996, a new complaints procedure for handling complaints about GPs was introduced. A new disciplinary system was also implemented at this time, which is separate from the complaints procedure. New paragraphs were added to the terms of service requiring GPs to:

- establish and operate practice-based procedures for dealing with complaints

- cooperate with investigation of complaints by health authorities (this may occur if a complainant is not satisfied with the outcome of a practice-based investigation).

Inquiries about prescriptions and referrals

The GP should be prepared to answer any inquiries from the health authority relating to:

- any prescriptions issued
- referrals to other NHS services.

Annual reports

A GP or partnership should provide the health authority annually with a report containing the information in Box 3.13. The information in paragraph 3 of the table need only be supplied if the health authority requests it, having considered whether the information is available from another

---

Box 3.13: Information to be provided in annual reports

1 particulars of the doctor's other commitments as a medical practitioner, including:

   (a) a description of any posts held, and
   (b) a description of all work undertaken

   and including, in each case, the annual hourly commitment, except that where a doctor has notified the health authority of such other commitments in a previous annual report the report need only contain information relating to any changes in those commitments

2 as respects orders for drugs and appliances, the doctor's arrangements for the issue of repeat prescriptions to patients

3 information relating to the referral of patients to other services under the Act during the period of the report:

   (a) as respects those by the doctor to specialists:
      (i) the total number of patients referred as inpatients
      (ii) the total number of patients referred as outpatients

   by reference in each case to which clinical specialty applies, and specifying in each case the name of the hospital concerned; and

   (b) the total number of cases of which the doctor is aware (by reference to the clinical specialty) in which a patient referred himself to services under the Act

---

Box 3.13: *continued*

4 information relating to the numbers of patients on the doctor's list:
   (a) who are diabetic
   (b) who are asthmatic, and
   (c) to whom the doctor has given advice, in accordance with paragraph 12(2) of Schedule 2, about:
       (i)   the patient's weight
       (ii) the use of tobacco, or
       (iii) the consumption of alcohol
5 number of complaints received under the practice-based procedure

---

source and having consulted the LMC. Similarly, information in paragraph 4 need only be supplied if the health authority requests it and if the GP is not already supplying the information to qualify for health promotion or chronic disease management payments. Each report should be compiled for a 12-month period ending 31 March and sent to the health authority by 30 June.

Conclusion

This commentary is selective, not comprehensive. Not all paragraphs in the terms of service have been covered and only a brief summary of those referred to has been provided. If any problem arises, GPs should refer to the regulations and if necessary seek advice and assistance from the LMC or BMA local office.

4 Fees and allowances

Where to obtain advice and assistance

BMA members can contact their local BMA office for expert advice and assistance. Help can also be obtained from health authority and LMC offices. The BMA web site is at www.bma.org.uk

Further reading includes Ellis N and Chisholm J (1997) *Making Sense of the Red Book* (3e). Radcliffe Medical Press, Oxford, and the Red Book itself.

The pay system for GP principals is complex and hard to understand. GP principals earn their income from a range of fees and allowances. These are of four broad types: fixed allowances, capitation-based payments, item-of-service payments and bonus payments. They are set each year at levels which will both yield the finite 'pool' of money available to fund GPs' net income and meet those expenses not reimbursed directly by the health authority. The 'pool' that funds GPs' net income is calculated by multiplying average intended net remuneration (decided by government on the advice of the Review Body) by the number of GP principals.

If the relative level of any fee or allowance is altered (e.g. by increasing the basic practice allowance or decreasing capitation fees), the remaining fees and allowances are changed so that the total amount of money paid out to GP principals remains at the right level. Unless additional funds are specifically made available by government (colloquially known as 'new money'), according to the current pay system it is not possible to increase any specific fees or allowances without simultaneously reducing some other fee(s) so as to maintain the level of net remuneration.

This chapter outlines the main fees and allowances. Full details of all fees and allowances are given in the Statement of Fees and Allowances (also known as the SFA or Red Book).

Basic practice allowance

A basic practice allowance (BPA) is paid if a GP principal's individual list size or the partnership average list size is at least 400 patients; a GP with at least 400 patients is paid a BPA and its level increases with list size up to a ceiling of 1200 patients. Thus a lump sum is paid for the first 400 patients and additional capitation payments are then made for each patient between 400 and 600, 600 and 800, 800 and 1000, and 1000 and 1200. By weighting the level of these capitation payments in favour of the lower list size, the BPA is designed to compensate for the proportionately greater standing expenses incurred by a small practice than a larger one. The BPA is also weighted in favour of part-time GPs; that of a half-time GP is significantly greater than half that of a full-time GP.

Deprivation payments

A capitation-based supplement to the BPA, known as the 'deprivation payment', is paid for all patients living within an area classified as 'deprived' according to the Jarman deprivation index, whether or not the individual or family is actually deprived. This supplement is intended to reflect the higher workload associated with some categories of patients. GPs with individual or average partnership lists of less than 400 patients who are not paid a BPA, nevertheless qualify for deprivation payments for patients living in deprived areas. There are different levels of payment according to the degree of deprivation (as measured by the Jarman index) of the area where the patient lives.

Where the average number of patients per principal is above 2500, payments will be capped at that level unless the practice can demonstrate that it is providing the following services:

- child health surveillance; or ensuring that appropriate alternative arrangements are available locally
- contraceptive services
- cervical cytology – achieving lower-rate target payments
- childhood immunisations – achieving lower-rate target payments

- health promotion services in accordance with the SFA
- chronic disease management programmes for asthma and diabetes.

All partners should be in receipt of postgraduate education allowance (PGEA).

Seniority payments

There are four levels of seniority payment:

- the first level is paid to a GP registered for 10 years or more who has been providing general medical services or in HM Forces for at least six years
- the second level if paid to a GP registered for 17 years or more who has been providing general medical services or in HM Forces for at least 13 years
- the third level is paid to a GP registered for 23 years or more who has been providing general medical services or in HM Forces for at least 19 years
- the fourth level is paid to a GP registered for 29 years or more who has been providing general medical services or in HM Forces for at least 25 years.

Pro rata payments are made to part-time GPs and those full-time GPs not eligible for the full BPA. Job sharers are assessed for the seniority payment on an individual basis and payment is reduced pro rata according to their hours of availability.

Capitation fees

The standard capitation fees are paid at three rates according to a patient's age: under 65 years, 63–74 years, and 75 years and over.

Registration fee

This is paid for carrying out certain health checks on newly registered patients (except those aged under five years), normally within three months of them joining the doctor's list.

Postgraduate education allowance

The PGEA is paid to any GP principal who undertakes a programme of continuing education; it is intended to cover any course fees, travel and subsistence costs.

To receive the full rate of the PGEA, GPs must demonstrate to their health authority that they have attended an average of five days' training a year over the past five years. Although the amount of time spent on courses may vary from year to year, a GP is expected to achieve a reasonable balance between years. Courses are divided into three areas:

- health promotion and prevention of illness
- disease management
- service management.

To claim the PGEA, GPs have to attend at least two courses under each of the three subject areas over the five years preceding the claim. The length of course is not actually defined in the Red Book; postgraduate deans have discretion to determine what constitutes a 'course' for the purpose of completing a balanced educational programme.

A GP should claim the allowance from the health authority each year, giving details of courses attended over the five-year period. Any GP who meets the required criteria (25 days' training and at least two courses under each of the three headings) is paid a full PGEA in quarterly instalments. Lower levels of the allowance are paid if courses are spread across only one or two of the subject areas or if less than the maximum length of training is undertaken.

Target payments for childhood immunisation and cervical cytology

In 1990, the government introduced target payments for childhood immunisation and cervical cytology. There are two levels of payment. For childhood immunisation, a higher level of payment is made to GPs who achieve 90% coverage and a lower level for 70% coverage. For cervical cancer screening the upper level is 80% and the lower 50%. These are calculated on a partnership basis.

Childhood immunisation

There are two target levels, 70% and 90%, and these relate to average coverage levels across four groups of immunisations:

- Group I   – diphtheria, tetanus and poliomyelitis
- Group II – pertussis
- Group III – mumps, measles and rubella (MMR)
- Group IV – *Haemophilus influenzae* type B (Hib).

A target is reached if, on average across the four groups, 70% or 90% of the children aged two years on a GP's list have had complete courses of immunisation (i.e. three doses of diphtheria, tetanus and poliomyelitis, or three doses of pertussis, or one dose of MMR, or three doses of Hib). To calculate this, the coverage level in each group is taken into account and the mean of these is the overall coverage level. For example, if a practice has ten children on the list aged two years, all of whom have had complete courses of diphtheria, tetanus, poliomyelitis and Hib, nine who have had a complete course of pertussis and eight who have had the MMR immunisation, the overall coverage level is nine out of ten, that is 90%. Thus, the higher target level has been reached. All complete immunisation courses count towards coverage levels whether done by the GP making the claim or some other person, such as a community health clinic doctor. The maximum payment a GP can receive depends on how many children aged two years are on the list; the Red Book describes how this is calculated. The proportion of the maximum payment made to a GP reflects the amount of this work done within general medical services, rather than in a clinic or hospital setting, whether in the patient's current practice or a previous one. Thus, if the 90% level is achieved, and GPs have done 70% of all the complete courses of immunisation, the claiming GP receives 7/9 of the maximum payment.

Pre-school boosters for children under five years

Again, there are two target levels: 70% and 90%. A target is reached if at least 70% or 90% of children aged five years on a GP's list have had reinforcing doses of diphtheria, tetanus and poliomyelitis immunisations. The arrangements for calculating these payments are similar to those described above.

Cervical cytology

There are two target levels: 50% and 80%. A target is reached if 50% or 80% of women on a GP's list aged 25–64 years in England and Wales (or aged 21–60 years in Scotland) have had an adequate cervical smear test during the previous five-and-a-half years. (This period is based on a five-year call/recall system with an allowance for unavoidable delays.) All smear tests are counted, not just those taken in general practice. For the purpose of calculating coverage, women who have had hysterectomies (involving the complete removal of the cervix) are excluded. The maximum size of the target payment a GP can receive depends on the number of eligible women on the list. The actual proportion of the maximum payment paid to a GP reflects the work done by GPs (and their staff) as opposed to others, such as the private sector and community health services.

Child health surveillance fee

To be paid for child health surveillance services a GP principal must also be on the health authority child health surveillance list; admission to this requires them to satisfy the criteria relating to experience and training set out in the regulations. A capitation supplement is paid for each child patient under the age of five years to whom a GP provides developmental surveillance, if the child is registered for this purpose.

Minor surgery payments

A sessional payment is made to GP principals on the health authority minor surgery list who personally provide minor surgery services. A session consists of at least five surgical procedures, performed either in a single clinic or on separate occasions. GPs can undertake minor surgery for patients on their own personal list or that of a partner or another member of the group practice. A GP is eligible for no more than three such payments in respect of any one quarter. However, a GP who is in a partnership or group may claim additional payments, provided the total number of payments to the partnership or group per quarter does not exceed three times the number of GPs involved. Up to four minor surgery procedures can be carried forward for inclusion in the following quarter's claim.

Night consultation fees and the night allowance

All GP principals are paid an annual night allowance in partial recognition of their 24-hour responsibility for patients. This allowance is paid at a flat rate per GP with job sharers counting as a single GP for this purpose.

In addition GPs are paid a fee for each face-to-face consultation requested and undertaken between 10 pm and 8 am with a patient who is:

- on their list of patients
- a temporary resident
- a woman for whom they had undertaken to provide maternity medical services in connection with which the consultation is provided.

Where the GP is separately engaged or employed by an NHS trust or health authority to provide services in any premises owned or managed by the trust or authority, the fee is paid only if the GP is not on duty or on call at those premises and the request for the patient to be seen was made in accordance with paragraph 13 of the terms of service. However, if the GP visits the patient in a hospital to provide maternity medical services, a consultation fee is paid if he or she holds an appointment at the hospital, but was not on duty at the time, or if he or she does not hold such an appointment in respect of maternity medical services.

The fee is paid to the doctor with whom the patient is registered, regardless of whether the visit is made by:

- the GP principal with whom the patient is registered
- a partner or another GP from the practice
- an assistant, associate, GP registrar, locum or deputy engaged by the partnership or group, or a doctor in the same out-of-hours rota.

Associate allowance

Single-handed GPs in very isolated areas (e.g. the Highlands and Islands) are eligible for an associate allowance, enabling them, in conjunction with other single-handed GPs, to employ an associate GP who can provide services for patients during absences for social and professional purposes.

Health promotion payments

A new payment system based on practices developing their own health promotion programmes was introduced in October 1996. The scheme is based on a single level of payment for health promotion activities approved by local, professionally led, health promotion committees. The amount a practice receives is related to list size.

Activities must relate to:

- modern authoritative medical opinion
- the *Health of the Nation* strategy and/or
- patient needs and/or
- local health priorities.

There are separate payments for organising chronic disease management programmes for either asthma or diabetes. These require practices to develop guidelines for delivering care to these patients.

Sustained quality payments

All GP principals qualify for an additional allowance for delivering quality patient services provided the practice meets the following benchmarks governing eligibility.

1 The practice should be able to report that all patients, where it is clinically appropriate, are able to obtain a consultation within 24 hours of requesting it.

2 The practice should be able to demonstrate that each component of the patient record is in date order, joined with tags where appropriate and contained in an adequate file or envelope. Practices where records are normally held on computer should be able to demonstrate the ability to transfer an appropriately structured record to facilitate patient transfer between practices. The benchmark for achievement is 80%.

3 The practice should be able to demonstrate that each patient and their care has been reviewed at appropriate intervals and an up-to-date list of repeat or continuing medication and a record of current and recent drug treatments (including dosage regimens) are kept within the patient record.

4 The practice should be able to demonstrate that it achieves higher target payments for immunisation programmes and that it communicates

with parents or guardians of patients who miss vaccination in order to encourage greater uptake.

5 The practice should be able to demonstrate that for chronic disease management of diabetes, appropriate elements of the annual check are carried out in the practice on at least 50% of patients diagnosed with non-insulin dependent diabetes mellitus and that at least 80% of all patients with diagnosed diabetes mellitus receive a comprehensive annual review. For chronic disease management of asthma, the practice should be able to demonstrate that at least 80% of patients diagnosed with asthma have been offered supportive education programmes within the practice. For chronic disease management in a further field, the practice should show that in another area where there is a significant burden of morbidity that it has a policy of regular monitoring, managing and auditing for the patients in the practice.

6 The practice shall show that it has an up-to-date age/sex register for the practice with mapping of one morbidity field as well as diabetes and asthma and that it is able, because it has patient registers for asthma, diabetes and one other disease, to operate a call–recall system.

7 The practice should be able to demonstrate an increase in prescribing by non-proprietary title where this is less than 70% **and** be able to demonstrate that the majority of prescribing falls within a locally agreed and appropriate bandwidth **or** be able to demonstrate the use of a formulary.

Verification that the standards are achieved is undertaken by health authorities in consultation with LMCs. All training practices approved by the JCPTGP are deemed to qualify for payment.

Other fees and allowances

- additions to the BPA for employing an assistant
- inducement payments
- initial practice allowances
- mileage payments
- temporary resident fees
- fees for emergency treatment
- fees for immediately necessary treatment
- fees for maternity medical services
- fees for contraceptive services

- fees for public policy vaccinations and immunisations
- fees for service as an anaesthetist and for arresting a dental haemorrhage
- payments for supplying drugs and appliances
- payments during sickness and confinement – there are no list-size restrictions for employing a locum during confinement
- locum allowances for single-handed practitioners in rural areas attending educational courses
- prolonged study leave allowance
- GP registrar scheme payments
- doctors' retainer scheme payments
- payments under the rent and rates scheme
- improvement grants
- payments under the practice staff scheme
- payments under the computer reimbursement scheme.

Claiming correct fees and allowances

The remuneration system for GP principals is probably the most complex in the world. It takes several hundred pages and an estimated 350 000 words of the regulations and the Red Book to determine how and what a GP should be paid. Every practice should ensure that it is claiming correct fees and allowances, otherwise it will not receive its correct remuneration. Conversely, no claim should ever be made, whether knowingly or unknowingly, for a fee or allowance to which a GP or practice is not entitled. False or improper claims can have very serious consequences. Health authorities have not hesitated to instigate criminal proceedings against GPs who have made these.

5   The partnership agreement

Where to obtain advice and assistance

BMA members should contact their local BMA office for general advice and assistance. Members can obtain free of charge an authoritative booklet, *Medical Partnerships under the NHS*, and a publication by the BMA General Practitioners Committee, *Partnership Agreements: guidance for GPs*. Health authorities and LMCs are also important sources of advice. However, both partners and prospective partners should also obtain independent legal advice when entering or substantially amending a partnership agreement, preferably from solicitors who are familiar with medical partnerships.

The BMA web site is at www.bma.org.uk

Further reading includes Ellis N and Stanton T (eds) (1994) *Making Sense of Partnerships*. Radcliffe Medical Press, Oxford.

The partnership provides a legal framework within which most GP principals work: less than 10% of practices are single-handed. Given its importance to the business of general practice, the widespread ignorance and neglect of the partnership agreement among the profession is quite remarkable.

Many practices do not have written partnership agreements; it has been estimated that at least half either have no written agreement or work to an outdated version. Any partnership without this essential documentation is susceptible to the vagaries that flow from the fact that relations between partners are strictly controlled by a statute more than a century old, the Partnership Act 1890. A partnership without a written agreement is

**Box 5.1: Key characteristics of a 'partnership at will':
one without a written agreement**

- entire partnership ends automatically upon death, retirement or bankruptcy of any one partner
- any partner can choose to end the partnership immediately without notice to the other partners, unless remaining partners elect to continue
- all partners must have free access to the bank account and are entitled to take part in managing the business
- partnership decisions may be made by a majority of the partners, except that all partners must consent to a new partner being admitted as well as to any change in the nature of the business
- no partner can be expelled from the partnership
- partners must not compete with the partnership; if they engage in any business on their own account in the same broad field of activity as the partnership, any income from this must be paid to the partnership
- all partners are regarded as 'agents' of the partnership and can take decisions and enter into commitments to which the whole partnership is bound

known as a 'partnership at will' and is governed by this Act; its main characteristics are listed in Box 5.1. However, a partnership can develop or agree to abide by rules which modify or add to those drawn from this legislation. Variations and departures from the Partnership Act can be inferred from the conduct of the partners; for example, although the Act requires profits to be shared equally, many practices opt for a different basis of division.

Given the dangers and potential difficulties of a 'partnership at will', it is surprising how many practices do not have written agreements. But neglect of essential paperwork has been commonplace in general practice; until comparatively recently most practice staff did not have written employment contracts, even though they were legally entitled to them.

The need for a written agreement

A partnership in any field can be plagued by problems, and general practice is no exception. Although a written agreement offers no panacea, it at least lays down ground rules which can help to resolve, if not avoid, problems. Once these rules are established, it is only sensible to take a step further by writing them down clearly and unambiguously so that all partners know exactly where they stand.

Partnership disputes are widespread and can present particularly intractable problems. GP partnerships typically experience enough problems and difficulties in normal times. The continual changes in regulations and employment law and the resultant paperwork have increased these problems and placed further pressures on GP partnerships. While an agreement cannot prevent disputes, it can help to avoid many common problems and frequently resolve those which occur by specifying procedures to be followed when a dispute arises or a partnership breaks up.

A written agreement should not slavishly follow some prescribed standard format. Rather, it must reflect the explicit wishes of the partners; only they know how they want to work together, the practice's circumstances and what problems need to be addressed.

What should be included in a written agreement

No written agreement, no matter how comprehensive, can be expected to define all the rights and obligations of the partners; many of these have to be inferred from their day-to-day working relations. Nevertheless, there is a well-established framework that is widely used and this normally includes the clauses covered by the headings in Box 5.2. Strictly speaking, many standard clauses covered by these headings are not necessary because the rights or obligations they assign are either prescribed by the Partnership Act 1890 or are always implied – for example, the obligation to be just and faithful in all dealings with one's partners, and to act in good faith towards each other (*see* Box 5.3). Nevertheless it is probably advisable to include them in the written agreement.

A written and comprehensive partnership agreement should ensure equity for all partners and reasonable security. Equity does not necessarily imply equality; an equitable partnership agreement should ensure that all partners are treated fairly. For example, the list sizes of individual partners should have no significance in respect of each partner's rights and

---

Box 5.2: Main headings in a partnership agreement

- date of document
- name, title and address of the partnership
- date when partnership commenced
- nature of the practice's business
- duration of partnership
- practice premises
- partnership capital
- partnership expenses
- partnership income
- sharing the profits
- attending to the affairs of the practice
- managing practice staff
- partnership decisions
- partnership taxation
- holidays and study leave
- maternity provisions
- prolonged incapacity and sickness
- voluntary and compulsory retirement from the partnership
- restrictive convenants
- defence body membership
- banking arrangements
- accounts
- arbitration/conciliation

---

obligations. It is taken as evidence of good faith if a new partner is able to acquire a comparable list size as soon as reasonably practicable.

The notes below outline issues that need to be addressed and what should be covered under each heading.

Date, name, title and address

Any agreement should specify a date of commencement, which may be earlier than the current date if it reflects an existing partnership, or a later

---

Box 5.3: A breach of good faith

A new partner joins a practice with a satisfactory partnership agreement. After two or three months, he suggests to the senior partner that it would be a good idea to employ a further practice nurse, adding that he knows someone who would be suitable. The senior partner agrees, and the practice nurse is taken on. The nurse becomes pregnant, and it is revealed subsequently that she is the live-in girlfriend of the new partner. According to the senior partner, a lot of patients are outraged by the situation, and he insists that the nurse stops work and, in fact, wants to dismiss her. According to the partnership agreement, no member of staff can be dismissed without the agreement of all the partners, and therefore the nurse remains on the payroll until such time as she goes on maternity leave. On the basis of advice from the partnership's solicitors, the other partners override the junior partner's opposition on the grounds that his original action, in recommending his girlfriend as an employee without disclosing his relationship with her, was in breach of the obligation to act in good faith towards his partners.

From the BMA's files

---

date if it relates to a new partnership. It must be signed by all partners before it is dated; any liability will begin on the commencement date, not the date of agreement, unless both are the same.

The agreement should also include the name under which the partnership will practise, and the addresses of the surgery premises. If the partnership uses any name which does not consist of the true surnames of all partners, the true names of each partner must be included on letter headings, invoices, etc., and displayed in each surgery, to meet the requirements of the Business Names Act 1985.

The nature of the business

A possible wording for this clause is that the partners 'will carry on the profession of NHS general medical practice'. It is essential to specify the nature of the business because this limits the extent to which each partner is liable as an agent of the firm. Otherwise, the liabilities arising from some other quite separate and extraneous business activity undertaken by one

---

Box 5.4: Extent of a partnership's liabilities: a partner's wider interests

A GP of 15 years' standing, who had worked solely in a three-man practice, started a business outside the practice with which the other two partners had no dealings, financial or otherwise. In 1991, two years afte the business started, it went into receivership.

The GP's assets were liquidated to satisfy his personal debts, and these included his share in the partnership business, its equipment, premises, etc.

From the BMA's files

---

partner might be incurred by the other partners, even though they had no direct interest or involvement in this other business. Box 5.4 illustrates the kind of problem that can arise.

Duration of partnership

There is no advantage in limiting duration; doing so reduces the security of all partners and can encourage them to compete among themselves in anticipation of the agreement's termination. Thus a partnership should be of indefinite duration: for the joint lives of all partners, or any two or more of them (*see* Box 5.5). Failure to state the duration of a partnership will

---

Box 5.5: Duration of partnership

The Partnership Act 1890 states that every partnership is dissolved in respect of all partners by the death or bankruptcy of any partner, unless there is agreement to the contrary. This is why every partnership agreement covering more than two partners should include a provision to the contrary.

'The partnership shall continue during the joint lives of the partners. The death, retirement, expulsion or bankruptcy of any partner shall not determine the partnership as regards the other partners.'

---

render it a partnership at will, which will mean that it can be dissolved at any time at the choice of any partner. However, once a partnership is created, it can be dissolved at any time by *mutual* consent.

Practice premises

An incoming partner should clarify ownership of surgery premises and any prospective liability to purchase a share. If the existing partners have a large investment in property and are seeking a contribution from a new partner, then he or she should seek *independent legal and financial advice*.

A new partner who is buying an equal share of the premises is entitled to an equal share of health authority direct reimbursement under the rent and rates scheme, even though parity in profit share may not be reached for several years. This important matter is often neglected if a practice simply treats this reimbursement as income and pays it into the partnership account before calculating profit shares.

The agreement should specify which partners are 'property owners'. If there is a lease or licence arrangement between the property-owning partners and other partners, it should be made only on the basis of legal advice and it is preferable that these arrangements are evidenced in a separate legal document. It is sensible if the partnership agreement defines the owners and confirms the rights of the other doctors to use the practice premises, and that the remaining partners should have a continuing right to use the premises for, say, three months if the property owner(s) leave the partnership.

Rent and rates payments from the health authority should normally be paid into the partnership bank account, being the property of the partnership as a whole (*see* Chapter 6 for a description of alternative ways of distributing these payments among partners, depending on their shares in ownership of the property).

Partnership capital

This normally includes all property, equipment, drugs, surgery fittings and furniture, together with any cash used as working capital. An incoming partner will buy a share of these assets and also contribute to the practice's working capital. Partners normally own shares of the assets (apart from the premises) in the same proportion as their share in the profits. The written agreement should specify how shares in the partnership's capital are divided among the partners (*see* Box 5.6), what constitutes the capital, and also confirm the arrangements for expanding the capital.

Box 5.6: Acrimony over who owned what

Dr A fell out with his partners Drs B and C and, as a consequence, dissolution of the partnership was discussed. There had been considerable discontent between the partners, which arose from a long period of study leave taken by Dr A. The partnership did not have a written agreement. When discussions took place about the partnership break-up, it was extremely difficult to disentangle the capital of the partnership from items individually owned by the partners. This sadly led to the demeaning scene of Dr A arguing in front of patients with Drs B and C over who owned which items of surgery equipment and furniture.

There was no statement of the capital assets and no inventory which the three partners could use in their discussions about dissolution. Consequently, the process was accompanied by considerable acrimony.

From the BMA's files

Partnership expenses

The agreement should specify which expenses should be paid by the partnership as a whole; typically these should include the cost of practice staff, accounting and banking services, telephone and stationery, and also the costs of occupying and running the premises (rent, rates, heating, lighting, cleaning and maintenance). All these shared expenses should be met before profits are calculated and distributed, and partners should contribute to them in proportion to their profit shares.

Other expenses, such as the costs of the partners' cars and home telephones, are normally paid by individual partners because this arrangement is usually fairer. Whichever arrangement prevails, it should be specified clearly in the agreement so that there can be no ambiguity and uncertainty about this crucial matter.

Partnership income

It is generally held to be advisable to include all earnings from professional practice in the partnership's income, otherwise individual partners might be encouraged to concentrate on those activities rewarded by personal rather than practice income and even compete among themselves for this type of work. However, it is possible with care to arrange a partnership's affairs to enable partners to retain their non-general medical services professional income and not to put the harmony of the partnership at risk.

Certain earnings are normally retained personally because they should not put at risk the collective efforts of the partnership (e.g. the seniority and postgraduate education allowances). Whatever arrangement is agreed, it must be equitable and should be defined in the partnership agreement (*see* Box 5.7).

Box 5.7: 'A postgraduate experience'

A new partner unwittingly signed a partnership agreement which allowed the other two partners to retain their seniority allowances and PGEAs, but required her PGEA to be paid into the 'pool' for distribution among all partners.

From the BMA's files

Dividing the profits

Stated simply, the profit (or loss) is the difference between practice income and expenses. The agreement should specify the size of each partner's share of the profits, and how it is calculated and paid. If changes in the share ratios are planned (e.g. a move to parity for a new partner), these need to be stated, including when they should take effect.

Under NHS regulations, for the health authority to recognise GPs as partners, it must be satisfied that they discharge the duties and exercise the powers of a principal in the partnership and that, unless an approved job sharer, they are entitled to a share of the profits (*see* Box 5.8) based on one of these options:

- if contracted to be available for at least 26 hours a week – a share of not less than one third of the partner with greatest share

---

Box 5.8: Salaried partners

This description is a contradiction in terms as far as it applies to any independent contractor. Someone is either a partner, with all the rights and obligations that entails, or they are not, in which case they are not a principal and the practice is not entitled, for example, to be paid a BPA (and its related allowances) for that doctor.

- if contracted to be available for between 19 and 26 hours – not less than one quarter of greatest share
- if contracted to be available for between 13 and 19 hours – not less than one fifth of greatest share.

If any partner's share is grossly out of line with his or her contribution to the work of the practice, a concealed sale of goodwill may be deemed to have taken place (*see* Box 5.9).

Box 5.9: Sale of goodwill is prohibited

The Medical Practices Committee (MPC) is responsible for issues concerning the sale of goodwill. Since 1948, GPs have been forbidden to sell the 'goodwill' of an NHS practice, 'goodwill' being the established custom and popularity of a practice. Examples of deemed sales of goodwill include:

- the premises are sold for substantially more than might have been expected if they had not previously been used for general practice
- a significant payment is made other than for undertaking partnership duties
- a partner receives a significantly less amount for his or her services than might reasonably be expected.

In particular, the MPC looks to see if the balance between profit share and workload is equitable.

The MPC may regard the following as evidence of a sale of goodwill:

- a new partner does not reach parity in the partnership profits within three years
- one or more partners is permitted to do less than a fair share of the practice workload
- one or more partners get longer or shorter holidays, or exceptionally is or is not entitled to study leave
- if, after a reasonable assessment period, a partner is restricted in taking on to his or her list any patient who chooses to register with him or her
- if the terms of expulsion, retirement or dissolution are not mutual.

Any GP about to join a practice who is concerned about a possible sale of goodwill may submit the terms of the proposed partnership to the Medical Practices Committee.

An incoming partner's share should be sufficient for it to be more than he or she might have earned as an assistant: this share should increase each year so that parity is reached within a reasonable time span, normally three years. He or she should not be prevented from taking a fair share of new patients on to his or her list (*see* Box 5.10).

Box 5.10: Exploiting a junior partner

Extract from a health authority general manager's letter:

'Dear Dr C

In reply to your request for information on the practice's arrangements for allocating patients to each partner's list, I can confirm that patients are divided:

Patients with surname	*To doctor*
A – end of Lane	A
Le – end of Watson	B
all remaining patients	C

I hope this information is helpful'

From the BMA's files

Attending to the affairs of the practice

The agreement should state the time and attention which partners are expected to give to the work of the partnership, especially if one partner is allowed to give less time than others to it. If the partners are required to devote their whole time to the practice, it is advisable for the agreement to stipulate that they should not engage in any other business or accept any office (e.g. local councillor) without the consent of the other partners.

In the present climate, time spent on medical politics (e.g. as an LMC, primary care group board or GPC member) should be allowed for in the agreement, preferably before the issue has to be faced.

Box 5.11: Discrimination is prohibited

It is unlawful for a partnership of any size to discriminate on the grounds of sex or marital status, and for a partnership of six or more partners to discriminate on grounds of colour, race, nationality (including citizenship) or ethnic or national origins:

- when appointing a new partner
- in the terms on which the new partner is offered a partnership
- by refusing, or deliberately neglecting, to offer a partnership

and where someone is already a partner:

- in the way he or she is afforded access to any benefits, facilities or services; or by refusing, or deliberately neglecting, to afford access to those benefits, facilities and services; or
- by dismissing the partner, or treating him or her unfavourably in any other way.

Managing practice staff

The agreement should specify who carries responsibility for staff matters. It is advisable that staff employed by the partnership should be engaged and dismissed only with the consent of all partners, otherwise a dismissed employee could pursue a successful dismissal claim against the partnership as a whole if all partners have not agreed on the dismissal (*see* Box 5.12). It is also essential that the agreement should prevent one partner answering or sending letters concerning employment matters without the consent of the other partners. In any circumstances, hastily written and ill-considered letters often cause problems.

Partnership decisions

According to the Partnership Act 1890, differences of opinion in the partnership are settled by majority decision unless the agreement specifies some other arrangement. A partnership must decide whether decisions are to be taken on the basis of majority voting and, if so, what size majority is required to endorse different types of decision.

Box 5.12: Staff dismissal led to partnership rift

A busy, urban, four-doctor partnership decided to make several significant changes in the organisation of its practice staff. These included introducing a new computer system, leading to an enlarged job description for the practice manager.

The senior receptionist was not happy about the changes and felt that the practice manager was usurping some of her work. Tension grew and came to a head when she had a blazing row with one of the partners. The latter discussed it with the other partner on duty and dismissed the receptionist that day. When the other two partners were informed, they felt the decision had been too hasty.

The senior receptionist immediately applied to the industrial tribunal claiming unfair dismissal. Strains appeared within the partnership and it split into two before the hearing. The two partners who had not been involved in the dismissal believed they had no responsibility or financial liability with regard to the industrial tribunal case.

The tribunal found in favour of the dismissed receptionist who was awarded almost £10 000. The doctors who had not been responsible for the dismissal believed that they were not liable for the payment. But lack of any reference in the partnership agreement to the dismissal of staff meant that all four partners were jointly responsible and liable to contribute to the damages.

From the BMA's files

How this question is approached usually depends on partnership size. In a partnership of three, partners may opt for unanimity on all decisions, whereas a partnership of six may consider that unanimity is too difficult to achieve and may regard a majority of four to two as a satisfactory basis for decisions. Whatever approach is adopted should be specified in the agreement. Where there are job-share partners, the agreement should specify whether they exercise a half or whole vote each.

Irrespective of how a partnership approaches routine decision making, major decisions which affect key features of the agreement should be taken only if there is unanimity. The nature (i.e. what subject they relate to) of such decisions should be defined in the agreement.

Taxation

Prior to 1996/97, liability for the income tax on the whole of the practice's net profits was a joint and several liability for each partner. Tax and NI for staff wages are, however, still a joint and several liability for each partner. The partnership agreement should therefore provide for enough funds to be set aside for tax liabilities, preferably in a separate bank or building society account designated for this purpose.

Box 5.13: Joint and several liability

Dr C, Dr D and Dr E were in a dispensing partnership. Dr E ran the dispensing part of the practice and Drs C and D did not question his figures or returns for this. Subsequently, Drs C and D were horrified to find that Dr E had been fraudulent to the tune of over £500 000. Dr E did not account to Drs C and D for this money. The health authority demanded repayment and the Inland Revenue demanded tax on it, and Drs C and D were held jointly and severally liable for repayment.

Holiday and study leave

Each partner's eligibility for leave should be on an equitable basis (*see* Box 5.14). When a locum is employed to cover holiday or study leave, expenses should normally be met by the partnership as a whole. It is advisable for the agreement to restrict the number of partners who can be

---

Box 5.14: Surprised by holiday arrangements

In a three-partner practice, a new partner signed a partnership agreement whereby he agreed to cover holiday periods, etc. The three partners also agreed that they would cover each other's holidays to avoid the cost of hiring locums. Unfortunately for the new partner he had neglected to take account of the fact that the other two partners were married to each other and took their holidays together. As a result the new partner found himself providing continuous cover for the whole practice for at least six weeks each year.

From the BMA's files

---

on leave concurrently and the maximum length of unbroken leave which can be taken.

Sickness and pregnancy

Partnerships can make various arrangements to pay for locums employed during prolonged absences. A simple method is for the absent partner to pay all the locum expenses. However, it is increasingly common for the partnership as a whole to pay the first few weeks of these expenses.

A partnership will infringe the Sex Discrimination Act if a pregnant partner is treated less favourably than a male partner with a distinctly male incapacity. Therefore a partner on maternity leave should not have to meet the full cost of a locum unless this arrangement also applies to sick leave. Box 5.15 outlines the BMA's recommended maternity leave arrangements.

Additional payments made by the health authority during sickness or confinement should be paid to the absent partner if he or she is responsible for locum expenses. The question of how long the partnership or the individual partner pay locum expenses needs to be decided in relation to the

---

Box 5.15: Recommended maternity leave arrangements

- 18 weeks' absence should be regarded as a minimum entitlement and the pregnant partner should have the right to determine for herself when the period of absence should start, in consultation with her own GP

- the practice should consider the question of funding the cost of a locum to cover the actual workload of the pregnant partner, not merely her hours of availability

- the partnership should agree on a maximum period of absence following which the partner's failure to return to work may justify compulsory expulsion from the partnership

- the exercise of a partner's right to maternity leave should not abolish her entitlement to pro rata holiday and sickness leave

- adoption: the partnership agreement should specify leave arrangements

A partnership agreement which provides for maternity leave on terms which are less advantageous than sick leave could be construed as evidence of indirect sex discrimination.

arrangements for insurance cover for income protection and/or locum expenses.

Leaving the partnership

The agreement should specify the conditions under which partners may retire, including the required period of notice. It is usually simpler if the period of notice expires on a quarter-day so as to coincide with quarterly health authority payments. Ideally, a retiring partner should be allowed some discretion in selecting a date for retirement which is most favourable for tax purposes. The notice itself should not be less than three months because health authorities are entitled to three months' notice before removing a GP's name from the NHS medical list.

According to the 1890 Partnership Act, a partner cannot be expelled by a majority decision unless the agreement permits this to happen. Thus the agreement should contain a clause which makes provision for the expulsion of a partner in specific circumstances, such as prolonged incapacity, mental ill health, removal or suspension from the medical register or NHS medical list, gross breaches of the agreement and bankruptcy. Although such a clause would confer a right to expel a partner in certain specific circumstances, like any clause it may be waived by mutual consent.

Most agreements require a partner to retire after a period of prolonged incapacity which prevents him or her from doing a fair share of the work for a period of six to 12 months. Naturally most partnerships wish to be as generous as possible in such circumstances, but because prolonged absence imposes a considerable burden on colleagues, it may be advisable to require an incoming partner to produce evidence of good health before the partnership agreement is signed. Any sickness provision should be seen to be reasonable and preferably have provision for independent medical opinion.

Retirement

All GPs are required to retire from NHS practice by or on their 70th birthday. Thus it is sensible to include in the agreement a requirement that each partner retire from the practice by or on this compulsory retirement date. It may be advisable also to include a clause which allows a partner to continue to practice as a partner in a non-NHS capacity beyond a certain age, if other partners agree.

The partnership should agree on a clear and fair policy on retirement before individual problems arise; difficulties can occur if a practice only considers the issue of its retirement policy when the retirement of an individual partner is under discussion.

The issue of retirement can be particularly contentious for any partnership. Younger and older partners often express differing views on the subject, and a partner's perception of the issue may alter as retirement approaches. Young doctors entering a partnership often prefer a clause requiring compulsory retirement at a specific age such as 60 years, because it reduces the risk of them having to support an old and possibly failing partner who is increasingly unable to do a fair share of the work. Such a clause may be attractive to partners when they themselves are comparatively young, but it becomes less attractive as retirement approaches.

Restrictive covenants

NHS legislation prohibits the purchase or sale of goodwill, but has not abolished goodwill as such. Thus it is legal to protect goodwill by reasonable restrictions on the future activities of a departing partner. Such restrictions are commonplace and usually enforceable. But any restraint must be entirely reasonable.

Any restrictive covenant must apply equally to all partners and relate only to work normally undertaken by a GP, and its duration should not be too long. Any restriction from working in a defined area must be reasonable; there should be a significant number of patients near to the boundary and it should not include any large concentrations of population which are of little or no significance to the practice. It may be advisable for the agreement to refer to the practice area map which would normally be a reasonable area in which to restrict an outgoing partner from practising. The map itself could be included in the agreement.

It is preferable to have a limited restraint clause which is capable of being enforced rather than a more draconian one which is unenforceable. Moreover, it is important to note that, in recent years, courts have taken an increasingly critical view of restrictive covenants. The Medical Practices Committee has issued important advice on restraint clauses (*see* Box 5.16), particularly in relation to the length of time and distance specified.

Defence body subscriptions

Each partner must be required to be a member of a medical defence organisation or hold appropriate medical indemnity insurance while a partner.

Banking arrangements

The agreement should name the partnership's bankers and specify the arrangements for signing cheques. All partners should be signatories to the

---

Box 5.16: Restrictive covenants: advice from the MPC

- the MPC looks at restrictive covenants to see if they are reasonable and mutual in their application. If the provisions are regarded as unreasonable or too restrictive, the MPC may consider this to be evidence of a sale of goodwill

- the MPC, in forming its opinion, normally regards as an acceptable upper limit a restrictive covenant which prevents a doctor engaging in NHS general practice and/or treating certain patients within a radius of two miles from the main premises for a period of two years. But variations may be justified by special circumstances

- the MPC would also consider there may be evidence of sale of goodwill if the radius and period were both reasonable but there was some extra restriction on a doctor acting within it in any capacity other than as a GP; for example, if it prevented the doctor from filling a hospital appointment within the radius

---

Box 5.17: Extract from a partnership agreement signed in 1990

'The partnership bank account shall be under the sole control of the principal partner and any cheque thereon shall be signed by him alone and the junior partner hereby appoints the principal partner as his attorney for all purposes in connection with the operation of the said bank account and the signing of cheques drawn thereon.'

From the BMA's files

---

account. However, the agreement should provide for at least two signatories for cheques over a set amount.

Box 5.17 shows a not untypical inequitable agreement in respect of a partnership's banking arrangement.

Partnership accounts

The agreement should name the partnership's accountants and specify arrangements for drawing up the accounts, including the date of the practice's financial year. It is normal to require all partners to sign the annual accounts for them to be binding.

All partners must have free access to the partnership's accounts and records. Any denial of access to any partner is strong *prima facie* evidence that the doctor concerned is in fact an employee, not a partner. It may be advisable to include in the agreement a provision that all partners and their agents (e.g. personal accountants) should have copies of the accounts.

Arbitration

However carefully drafted, no agreement can cover all contingencies. Disputes and differences of opinion can occur even in the most harmonious partnership. Most should be resolved within the partnership, sometimes with advice or assistance from the local BMA office, or even with assistance from an independent conciliator. Traditionally, the BMA has advised doctors to make provision in their partnership agreements for disputes to be referred by mutual agreement to independent arbitration. In practice, the use of arbitration should be very rare indeed. It is almost invariably an expensive process (usually much more costly than initially anticipated), more legalistic than is often assumed and, perhaps more important, often accompanies a final breakdown in the partnership and therefore does not contribute to its continuation (*see* Box 5.18). Thus though arbitration

---

Box 5.18: Sledgehammer to crack a nut?

In a partnership of seven, a majority of partners (six to one) decided to purchase pregnancy-testing equipment. The one partner opposed was very unhappy with the decision. He deemed this expenditure to be unnecessary and inappropriate, believing the provision of a pregnancy-testing service would result in its use prior to abortion. He also objected to the provision of such a service free of charge. He could not prevent his partners from offering this service to their patients, but he did not see why they should be doing so at the expense of the partnership; that is, partly at his own expense. The matter was referred to arbitration. The arbitration decision was lengthy and costly, and led ultimately to the dissolution of the partnership. All parties incurred several thousands of pounds of legal costs and the only outcome was a dissolution which was also costly.

From the BMA's files

---

may be appropriate in certain specific circumstances, these are more limited than is generally assumed.

The best advice to follow is for all partners to consider carefully the possible consequences of any action they may be contemplating, individually or collectively, which may precipitate arbitration and lead ultimately to the dissolution of the partnership. Any type of legal action, including arbitration, is almost invariably a costly option and is often associated with the break up of the partnership.

6 Surgery premises

Where to obtain advice and assistance

BMA members can obtain expert advice and assistance from their local BMA office. LMCs and health authorities are also important sources of information. Doctors should also consult their accountants and solicitors when planning the development of premises, and seek advice from architects and other specialists.

BMA Services can offer advice on the cost rent scheme and source and advise on the most suitable form of finance for you.

The BMA web site is at www.bma.org.uk

More information can be obtained from Kehoe S (ed) (1999) *Primary Health Care Premises: an expert guide*. Radcliffe Medical Press, Oxford, and Ellis N and Chisholm J (1997) *Making Sense of the Red Book* (3e). Radcliffe Medical Press, Oxford.

NHS general practice differs from other professions in that a substantial proportion of the cost of providing premises is directly met from public funds. This is because successive governments have wished to ensure that high standard surgery premises are generally available. Of course, NHS GPs also work within a different financial framework to those of other professions. They cannot simply raise income to fund premises by increasing their charges to clients, unlike for example accountants or solicitors. However, because public funds are at stake, the reimbursement of GPs' premises costs is subject to detailed and stringent controls, including rules specifying the amount of space eligible for reimbursement and how an appropriate level of rent reimbursement is assessed by the district valuer.

In practice, no single element in the reimbursement scheme is free from public scrutiny or control. Box 6.1 summarises these controls.

Box 6.1: Health authority controls over use of public funds for surgery premises

- government's district valuer advises on valuations to assess levels of notional rent payable
- government's district valuer advises on valuations relating to the cost rent scheme
- Red Book specifies minimum standards and maximum size of surgery premises eligible for reimbursement
- 'prescribed percentage' set by the Health Department determines level of cost rent payments

---

The terms of service require GPs to provide adequate surgery accommodation 'having regard to the circumstances' of the practice and to allow this to be inspected by the health authority and/or LMC. Virtually every GP principal is eligible to be reimbursed rent and rates for their surgery premises. But the health authority has to be satisfied that the use of existing premises, their enlargement or a move to new premises is in the interests of the NHS.

Although GPs can expect a high proportion of premises' costs to be directly refunded by the health authority, they often meet some of these costs themselves.

Surgery premises are usually provided in one of these ways:

- rented from a private landlord
- rented from a local authority
- rented from a health authority/NHS trust (often called health centres)
- owner-occupied by an individual GP or partners
- newly developed under the 'cost rent' scheme and owner-occupied by an individual GP or partners, or rented from a third party.

Primary Care Act pilot schemes can also expect health authority support for the provision of suitable premises. The terms should be similar to other GPs but must be negotiated directly with the health authority.

Rented surgeries

GPs who rent a surgery from a landlord can recover the cost of the rent from the health authority. An appropriate rent, as assessed by the district valuer, is repaid in full. If the premises are not used wholly for NHS work (e.g. if a part is sublet), an equivalent proportion of the rent is not reimbursed.

Health centres

The rent of GPs practising from health centres owned by health authorities/NHS trusts (together with their business and water rates) is normally paid by the health authority directly. Because it is not paid out from the practice's own funds and subsequently reimbursed, GPs should take particular care to ensure that both the rent and the equivalent amount of direct reimbursement are shown in their accounts. (Otherwise, if their accounts should be selected by the Inland Revenue for its anonymised sample of tax returns, their actual expenses will be assessed wrongly and this will adversely affect the Review Body's estimate of the level of average expenses due to be repaid indirectly to the profession as a whole.) The practice accountant should understand why these payments and reimbursements must be shown correctly.

Owner-occupied surgeries

In many cases, surgeries will not be rented from a third party but owned instead by the GPs themselves, either individually or in partnership. A rent allowance (notional rent) is therefore paid to recompense them for the use of their privately owned surgery for NHS purposes.

Valuation of GP premises

At present, incoming partners buying a share of practice premises must make a contribution based on the *vacant possession* valuation only of a building. Otherwise a sale of goodwill might be deemed to arise. In some circumstances, reduced property values may mean that such a valuation does not represent the full investment made in premises by an outgoing partner. Thus a conflict of interests can occur over valuations between incoming and outgoing partners. Partnership agreements should specify the method of valuation to be used.

Notional rent allowance

Notional rent is paid on owner-occupied surgeries that are neither new nor developed within the scope of the cost rent scheme; it is based on a district valuer's assessment of the current market rent which may reasonably be expected to be paid for the premises. It is paid quarterly or monthly to the practice and is reviewed triennially. Any practice that is not satisfied with its notional rent assessment may appeal against it.

Other reimbursements for premises

Health authorities may reimburse other costs relating to surgery premises, as shown in Box 6.2.

Box 6.2: Rent and rates scheme: types of direct reimbursement

- cost rents
- notional rents
- uniform business rates
- water rates
- sewerage rates
- sewerage charges
- water meter installation costs and charges
- refuse collection charges

These payments should be regularly and correctly claimed; practices are known to have foregone many thousands of pounds of income because they have failed to submit claims.

Some health authorities have introduced arrangements for paying rates and similar charges directly, which can improve a practice's cash flow. However, these payments and reimbursements, although they appear to be 'notional', must not be 'netted out' and thereby omitted from the practice's accounts.

Partnerships

It is usual for partnerships to own the surgery premises. But it is not uncommon for the partners to own them in differently sized proportions to the ratios which define their profit shares. For example, in a six-doctor partnership, two may be part-time or partially retired GPs not involved in surgery ownership, leaving the other four partners owning the building. One way of clarifying and simplifying ownership arrangements is to make a clear separation between the partnership formed for the purposes of providing general medical services and that formed to own and run the premises. The 'clinical' partnership can then treat the ownership of the premises as a quite separate exercise from the profit-sharing activities of the partnership. The 'property-owning' partnership charges rent to the profit-sharing partnership, which in turn receives notional rent income from the health authority. Alternatively, notional rent may be received by only the property-owning partners.

Improvement grants

Grants are available for improving surgeries and these are subject to health authority cash limits in the same way as cost rent schemes and practice staff reimbursement. These grants are paid only if a health authority has given prior approval to an improvement scheme and if the same expenditure is not also claimed as allowable expenditure against income tax. GPs should obtain advice from their practice accountant on whether to opt for an improvement grant or a tax allowance. If part of the cost of an improvement project does not qualify for a grant, tax relief can be claimed on the residual amount.

Grants are also available for buying practices, in unsuitable accommodation, out of their leasehold agreements. Applications are approved by health authorities if they are deemed to represent value for money and to be in the interests of improving services to patients.

Taxation

The notional rent allowance is paid to GPs whose privately owned surgeries are used for NHS general practice. It is essential for tax purposes that this is not treated or regarded as 'rent' in the usual sense of the word. In particular, it should not be treated as the private, unearned income of

GPs and it should not be included in the property section of the tax return. Otherwise, it could have a detrimental effect on how it is taxed and on whether retirement relief is granted for capital gains purposes.

New surgery development: the cost rent scheme

Most new or 'substantially improved' surgeries are funded by the cost rent scheme. Instead of being reimbursed at the current market rate (known as 'notional rent'), a GP may be reimbursed the cost of providing separate purpose-built premises (known as 'cost rent') if they are:

- completely new
- acquired and substantially modified
- already used and substantially modified.

An essential feature of the cost rent scheme is its recognition of the difference between the cost of providing an existing surgery and that of an entirely new or substantially improved surgery. It does not directly reimburse the actual interest paid on a loan for the cost of a building project. A practice should therefore ensure that its project is financially sound before entering into any commitment. It should be certain that the cost of servicing and repaying the loan can be met from the cost rent income, other practice income or (if necessary) funds from private sources.

The cost rent allowance is calculated by multiplying the cost of the project by a 'prescribed' percentage: for either a variable or fixed rate loan, according to the particular funding arrangement employed. To illustrate, if a project's total cost is £1 000 000 and the current fixed rate for the purpose of calculating cost rent is 6%, the annual cost rent payment to the practice is £60 000.

The four main cost components of a cost rent project are:

- buying the land
- erecting or modifying the building
- architectural and other professional fees
- bridging loan interest.

Because health authority funds for cost rent projects are cash limited, before entering into any commitments practices should:

- obtain health authority agreement 'in principle' to the project
- ascertain its priority in the health authority overall programme
- find out when cost rent payments will actually be made.

Not only must approval be obtained for the project, but the health authority should state whether it has sufficient funds for the scheme within its development programme and when they will be available.

The health authority's formal written offer should:

- confirm that the project is accepted for cost rent reimbursement
- specify the method used to calculate the level of reimbursement
- give an interim estimate of the level of reimbursement (interim cost rent)
- give a target date when reimbursement should start.

This written offer will be conditional upon the project being completed within a given timescale; if this is not possible the health authority may withdraw approval (without any obligation to meet any expenses the practice has already incurred).

GPs must ensure that they have planning permission and that their architects are aware of the cost rent scheme, particularly its limits on size and building costs as set out in the Red Book (SFA). These cost limits are defined for each health authority and reflect regional variations in building costs.

Cost rent limits

The maximum amount that can be spent on building a surgery is strictly limited. Many practices find it difficult to keep within these limits and have had to finance significant shortfalls from their own resources.

When the health authority has determined the total costs that can be included in the scheme, it calculates the amount of cost rent to be reimbursed by multiplying that sum by a 'prescribed percentage'. There are two percentage rates 'prescribed' by the Health Department: a variable rate, which is reviewed annually, and a fixed rate, which is reviewed quarterly.

The variable rate of reimbursement applies to projects funded by a variable rate loan, whereas the fixed rate applies to those wholly or mainly funded from a practice's own money or a fixed rate loan. If the fixed rate loan includes an option to switch to a variable rate, the fixed rate of reimbursement prevails until this choice is made.

Raising money for a cost rent project

When the project has been approved by the health authority, the next step is to raise money to fund it. Cost rent payments to a practice are calculated according to a fixed formula (which may be subject to some minor modifications) that takes no account of how the practice raises its funds. The actual process of obtaining the loan and agreeing interest and repayment rates is a totally separate matter. This distinction is crucial. The 'prescribed' percentage rate is deemed by the Health Department to be a reasonable average level of return on capital; it takes no account of the idiosyncrasies of the loan market or the varying ability of practices to raise loans. Thus there may be a significant difference between the income received from the cost rent allowance and the expenditure incurred on the loan.

Banks, insurance companies and building societies provide long-term loans for cost rent projects. Although the mortgage offers security to the lender in the event of a practice defaulting on its loan, it could be argued that the actual 'security' is the income paid to the practice through the cost rent scheme. Normally this income will continue to be paid uninterrupted for as long as a surgery is deemed by the health authority as being used to provide NHS practice, unless the practice opts to change to notional rent. Nevertheless, the lender will wish to be satisfied that the practice can service and repay the loan according to its agreed terms, because the cost rent income can be less than the cost of servicing the debt. If there is a shortfall between cost rent income and loan repayment, this has to be met from practice income unless the partners have access to private resources. This current or future liability must be assessed at the outset by the partners according to their personal circumstances, so that each partner can decide how the shortfall should be funded.

Changing to notional rent

The Red Book (SFA) recognises that current market rent (notional rent) is unlikely to produce initially a higher level of reimbursement than cost rent, therefore cost rent is paid until a practice opts to change to notional rent. But once this switch is made it cannot be reversed.

A review of notional rent can be requested:

- every three years from the operative date of the cost rent if the premises are owned by the practice

OR

- (if the premises are leased by the practice) when the rent due under the lease is reviewed or a new lease is entered into at the expiry of the existing lease.

Notional rent will be reviewed every three years after the date of assessment.

The decision to switch depends on several factors. Clearly, notional rent must exceed cost rent, and in the longer term a practice may feel relatively secure in the knowledge that property values and rents have (with some notable exceptions) tended to rise steadily year on year. However, recent years have shown that property and rental values can fall substantially. The average time taken for 'notional rent' to overtake 'cost rent' used to be in the range of seven to nine years. A significant problem can occur if practices switch from cost to notional rent only to find on triennial review that their notional rent falls to a level which is below the original cost rent. There are GPs who have found that the value of their equity in premises has fallen below their original investment and, instead of realising a gain at retirement, are faced with the prospect of having to repay a considerable sum to the partnership to reflect this.

Clearly, a practice should assess carefully at the time of review how much more reimbursement would be paid, likely future movements in interest rates, and the projected economic and political climate during the period prior to the next review of the prescribed variable rate.

7 Employing practice staff

As employers, GPs are subject to an extensive range of employment law. A plethora of legislation has been enacted by government to encourage a more formal and equitable approach to industrial relations and personnel matters. Other influences affecting this legislation have included comparisons with international standards (e.g. the Equal Pay Act and Sex Discrimination Act and European legislation on maternity leave) and legislation in other fields such as the Disability Discrimination Act and Race Relations Act. Although this law is intended to influence personnel practices in all organisations, the needs of the small employer, whose circumstances and resources differ greatly from those of the large organisation, have often been overlooked by the legislators. Although there are some minor concessions to size, the totality of employment law (as illustrated in Box 7.1) imposes a far greater administrative burden on small employers.

The overriding aim of any employer should be to avoid litigation. This can be achieved by good management practice, which means taking a more formal approach to many employment matters, such as preparing written employment contracts. For instance, small businesses often fail to issue written contracts of employment to staff (even though the law requires that this should be done) and rely instead on informal and undocumented understandings, which are often a recipe for disaster.

Box 7.1: Individual employment rights

Individual rights	Eligibility (length of service)
To be given a minimum period of notice – based on length of service – of termination of employment	Four weeks
To be given written particulars of terms of employment	Eight weeks
To receive equal pay with a member of the opposite sex doing similar work	None – applies immediately
Not to be discriminated against on the grounds of marriage or sex	Any stage from advertising of job
Not to be discriminated against on the grounds of colour, race, nationality, or ethnic or national origins.	Any stage from advertising of job
Not to be discriminated against on grounds of disability	Any stage from advertising of job (applies if 16 or more employees)
Not to be unfairly dismissed	One year
Not to be dismissed on pregnancy or childbirth grounds	None – applies immediately
To take 18 weeks' maternity leave	None – applies immediately
To return to work up to 29 weeks after week in which childbirth occurs	One year
To have unpaid time off for public duties	None – applies immediately

Box 7.1: *continued*

Individual rights	*Eligibility (length of service)*
To have time off – with pay – to seek alternative work or to arrange training if made redundant	Two years*
To receive statutory minimum paid holidays	None – applies immediately
To receive an itemised pay statement	None – applies immediately
To receive on request a written statement of the reason for dismissal	Two years (immediately and automatically if for pregnancy reasons)
To have paid time off for antenatal care	None – applies immediately
To be paid at least the national minimum wage	None – applies immediately
To have unpaid time off for paternity and special domestic leave	None – applies immediately

*If dismissal is for certain inadmissible reasons – that is, for reasons of trade union membership or activities, maternity or childbirth, or discrimination – there is no length of service qualification.

Brief mention should be made of radically new rights to trade union recognition which apply to any employer with 21 or more employees. These rights effectively enable as few as seven employees out of a workforce of 21 to bring about trade union recognition.

The remainder of this chapter summarises these key aspects of employment legislation:

- the employment contract: what it should contain and how to change it
- statutory maternity leave and pay
- disciplinary and dismissal procedures
- discrimination.

The employment contract

A contract of employment exists as soon as an employee demonstrates an acceptance of an employer's terms and conditions of employment by starting work. Both employer and employee are then bound by the terms offered and accepted. Often the initial agreement is verbal not written, but within two calendar months of any employee starting work the employer is legally obliged to provide a written statement detailing the main terms of employment, including a note on disciplinary procedures.

This written statement must contain the following information:

- names of parties to the contract
- date employment began and statement about continuity of employment
- job title or brief description of the work
- place of work
- pay, scale or rate of remuneration, intervals between payment
- hours of work
- holiday entitlement and holiday pay (there is now a statutory minimum right to four weeks' paid holiday)
- sick pay and sick leave
- pension arrangements
- notice of termination or length of contract
- grievance, disciplinary and appeals procedures (employers with less than 20 employees are exempt from including information on the disciplinary procedure).

It is also advisable, though not obligatory, to include information on:

- retirement policy
- maternity provisions
- health and safety policy.

It is sensible to prepare and issue a comprehensive contract of employment that covers all these subjects. (Members can obtain a model employment contract from their local BMA office.)

Attention paid to preparing a correct contract of employment should prevent unforeseen and unwanted disputes. The actual process of preparing and agreeing a contract should ensure that the practice is reasonably familiar with its legal responsibilities and obligations, and has not unknowingly acted contrary to these at the outset. Moreover, if any dispute should arise and a practice has to defend its personnel practices and policies, its position is greatly strengthened if it can show that it acted in good faith and took reasonable steps to conform with the law.

The statutory requirement to provide written statements on these matters does not have to be supplemented in any way. Although there is no legal obligation to provide a written contract as such, in practice a written statement of the main particulars of employment (together with a policy statement on health and safety) can be regarded as the basis of a written employment contract. The contract as a whole also includes the job description (whether written or not), and the many informal and undocumented understandings and working practices which inevitably form an important part of any employment contract. An example of these informal and unwritten practices are the arrangements applying to staff coffee and tea breaks.

A written contract may have to be changed. No difficulties should arise if the correct procedure is adopted and the substantive reason for the change is 'reasonable'. There are various ways of changing a contract and the key underlying principle is that an employee should normally consent to any changes before they can become contractually binding, irrespective of whether this consent is implied or, by express agreement, given in advance of or at the time of the change.

Obviously, an employer should seek to reach agreement on the proposed changes. If consent is obtained this can be given by express agreement, either orally or preferably in writing. In any case, an employer is required to put in writing the changed terms of the contract if they relate to any of the obligatory subjects listed above. Alternatively, consent may be demonstrated by implied agreement which can normally be assumed if an employee continues to work under the new contractual terms without complaint.

The written contract itself may contain provisions that allow for changes in matters such as pay, place of work, working hours and duties of the job. Nevertheless, even if a contract is drafted broadly, an employer must be prepared to show that the change itself is reasonable and was implemented in a reasonable way.

If consent is not forthcoming, even though the employer has made considerable efforts to agree the change with staff, unilateral implementation requires a reasonable period of notice. Normally, any contractual change imposed by an employer without an employee's consent will be a breach of contract, and if this is a fundamental breach (striking at the heart of the contract), an employee may be entitled to claim compensation for unfair dismissal. But by giving sufficient notice of the change, normally at least as long as that required to terminate the contract, it may be possible to avoid these problems. However, even if this length of notice is given, an employer could still be liable to pay compensation for unfair dismissal or redundancy. The advantage of giving adequate notice of change is that the employee is usually left with little or no time to protest after it is actually introduced.

In summary, the reasonableness of any change to an employment contract is subject to both a procedural test and a substantive test. Two questions have to be addressed and be capable of being answered in the affirmative:

- have you proceeded in a reasonable way by seeking agreement and giving adequate notice?
- is the proposed change itself a reasonable one to make in the particular circumstances of the business?

Statutory maternity rights

Most practices employ only a small number of staff, a large majority of whom are women. The employment rights of the expectant mother are intricate and stringent; thus, any employer can face serious administrative problems if staff become pregnant.

The six main employment rights of the expectant mother are:

- not to be unreasonably refused paid time off work for antenatal care (applicable to all employees irrespective of length of service)
- to take 18 weeks' maternity leave
- to take 40 weeks' maternity leave and return to work if she has at least one year of service
- to receive 18 weeks' statutory maternity pay (SMP) if she has 26 weeks' recent continuous employment and normal weekly earnings above the NI lower limit
- to complain of unfair dismissal if dismissed because of pregnancy or childbirth
- to return to work after absence on account of pregnancy or confinement.

This area of employment law is complex for both employer and employee. It is vital that GPs obtain detailed guidance on how to ensure an employee obtains her statutory maternity rights; each practice should have a copy of the Department of Social Security free booklet *Employer's Manual on Statutory Maternity Pay*. Any mistake, even if due to ignorance or misunderstanding of the law, could lead to a tribunal case and costly compensatory award. Industrial tribunals are assiduous in upholding pregnant employees' rights and impose severe penalties in cases where unfair dismissals have occurred because of pregnancy or childbirth.

Disciplinary procedures and dismissal

Employers are required to include details of their disciplinary procedures and the rules governing an appeal against disciplinary action in their employment contracts, or to specify where these are to be found. (Although employers with fewer than 20 employees are exempted from this requirement, it is advisable for all of them to do so.)

Disciplinary rules and procedures should promote fairness and order in the treatment of individual employees. They help a practice to run effectively by setting standards of conduct and performance, and ensuring that these are followed; they should not be seen primarily as a means of imposing sanctions. Their main purpose should be to emphasise and encourage improvements in individual employees' conduct and performance.

Employees who have not completed one year's continuous employment cannot normally complain of unfair dismissal, except if the dismissal is for an inadmissible reason such as pregnancy or childbirth.

The risk of a successful claim of unfair dismissal (which can involve compensation payments of several thousands of pounds) can be largely avoided if the procedure adopted is fair and reasonable, and the reasons for the dismissal are also fair and reasonable. A practice may have to justify its actions in an industrial tribunal so it is wise to keep detailed documentation throughout.

Several key principles related to retiring age affect an employee's rights to complain of unfair dismissal:

- if normal retiring age is the same for men and women no one may complain of unfair dismissal after that age, whatever it is
- if there is no normal retiring age, anyone under the age of 65 years may complain of unfair dismissal
- if normal retiring age is discriminatory (e.g. 60 years for women and 62 years for men), anyone under 65 years may complain of unfair dismissal.

Normal retiring age is ascertained from the reasonable expectations of employees and may differ from contractual retiring age. It may also vary between posts and grades.

Redundancy

Redundancy is still rare among practice staff but it has become more commonplace as practices have adjusted to the exigencies of the 1990 contract. Regrettably, unfair dismissals on the pretext of redundancy are more common; it is often thought that redundancy offers a more palatable way of getting rid of an unwanted employee.

If a redundancy occurs, important legal obligations fall on the employer. Employees have a statutory right to receive redundancy payments and paid time off from work to look for another job if they have at least two years' service and work at least eight hours a week. These same qualifying conditions also determine whether the employee has the right to claim unfair dismissal if a redundancy selection has not been made fairly according to objective criteria.

Under employment legislation redundancy is defined as a dismissal caused by an employer's need to reduce the number of staff. Normally an identifiable area of work should have disappeared or been reduced. A dismissal cannot be regarded as a redundancy if the employer immediately engages a direct replacement. But an employee with different skills or in a different location may be engaged (unless the redundant employee could be required under the contract of employment to work at the other location).

Normally any employee of a practice, when it changes hands, automatically becomes an employee of the 'successor' practice on the same terms and conditions of employment. It is as if the employee's contract had originally been made with the new practice; continuity of employment is preserved, as are any rights acquired under the old contract. So when staff are transferred in this way no dismissal has occurred and thus there is no entitlement to a redundancy payment.

An employer must make a statutory lump sum redundancy payment to any employee with at least two years' continuous service, working at least eight hours a week, who is dismissed because of redundancy.

Self-employed people or members of a partnership do not qualify.

The amount of the lump sum payments depends on how long the employees have been continuously employed, how these years of service relate to particular age bands and their weekly pay. An employee does not pay tax on statutory redundancy payment and an employer may set it off against tax as a business expense.

As far as possible, objective criteria, precisely defined and capable of being applied in an independent way, should be used when determining who is to be made redundant. This ensures that employees are not unfairly selected for redundancy. Examples of these criteria include length of service, attendance record, experience and capability. They should be applied consistently by any employer irrespective of the size of the business.

Great care must be taken if a practice is considering a redundancy, otherwise it could be faced with a claim for compensation for unfair dismissal. BMA members should contact their local office at the earliest opportunity for expert advice on how to handle this difficult situation. Far too often redundancy has been used as a pretext for dismissing employees who are not in fact redundant. The consequences of using redundancy to dismiss an employee who should otherwise be dismissed on grounds of inefficiency or incapacity, where there is no genuine redundancy, can be very serious indeed. A successful claim for unfair dismissal can require an employer to pay an employee a five-figure compensatory award. This compensation cannot be offset against taxation, nor can any part of it be reimbursed by the health authority.

Discrimination in employment

GPs should rarely experience any difficulties with the race and sex discrimination laws. Of course, avoiding discrimination *per se* is good management practice. It may seem unlikely that a small business with only a small number of employees (most of whom are women) could be affected in any way. But both the Race Relations Act and the Sex Discrimination Act apply to all employers, irrespective of size. Previously the Sex Discrimination Act applied to all employers apart from those with five employees or fewer; the government recently removed this exemption. The Disability Discrimination Act applies to employers with 16 or more employees.

There are three areas where legislation requires employers to act (and to be able to show that they have acted) in a manner that is not discriminatory on grounds of:

- sex and marital status
- colour, race, nationality (including citizenship), or ethnic or national origins
- disability.

If a practice's recruitment and selection procedures, together with its employment practices, are properly conducted, no difficulties should normally arise. Although sex discrimination legislation was primarily intended to improve the employment status and opportunities of women, GPs, whose practice staff are almost exclusively female, should remember that men have equal rights under this legislation.

The scope and structure of both sex and racial discrimination law are similar. Both specify two types of discrimination (direct and indirect) and both require employers to take essentially the same action so as to ensure their employment practices are neither discriminatory in practice nor capable of being interpreted as such.

Direct discrimination occurs when a person treats another person less favourably on grounds of race (or sex, or both) than he or she treats (or would treat) someone else. It is not necessary to show that the person openly expressed an intention to discriminate: it is possible in many instances to infer that the motive was discriminatory in the light of the circumstances of his or her actions.

Indirect discrimination occurs when the treatment may be equal in a formal sense but is discriminatory in its effects on one sex or particular racial group; for example, an unnecessary stipulation that a cleaner should have certain educational qualifications (e.g. GCSEs) which are not required for the job. When assessing whether an employer has acted in an indirectly discriminatory manner an industrial tribunal is required to consider whether his or her actions, although formally applied in a non-discriminatory manner, have the effect of being discriminatory.

There are three areas where it is unlawful to discriminate on grounds of race or sex when recruiting staff:

- in the arrangements for deciding who should be offered a job
- in relation to the contractual terms offered
- by refusing or deliberately omitting to offer a person employment.

It is also unlawful for employers to discriminate on grounds of sex or race in promotion or training opportunities, and in relation to any other benefits, facilities or services they provide for employees.

The most important matters on which a practice may need to concentrate are its arrangements for selecting and recruiting staff. The more informal its methods, the greater the risk of being accused of discrimination. An approach based on an informal 'word-of-mouth' method can easily leave an employer open to a claim (even from someone unknown to the practice who has not actually applied for a vacancy) that the selection procedure is discriminatory.

Finally, the 1995 Disability Discrimination Act requires any practice with 16 or more employees not to discriminate against disabled persons in relation to recruitment, selection, promotion or dismissal, by failing to make 'reasonable adjustments' to working arrangements or physical features at the workplace. Disability discrimination is defined as treating a disabled person less favourably than others.

8 Working in GP and community hospitals

Many GPs do some hospital work, usually in a local GP or community hospital. The contracts under which they work are varied and often include informal understandings which reflect long-standing working arrangements. In the past, contractual matters have been seriously neglected and GPs have sometimes given their services virtually free of charge to their local community. However, in recent years GPs have expressed increasing disquiet with their contractual arrangements and some practices have sought to improve these; having seen the NHS embrace the market philosophy they themselves are less willing to allow their goodwill to be exploited.

It is advisable to exercise great caution in the present NHS climate before taking any steps to change contractual arrangements. Many GPs in these hospital posts have very little security of tenure, particularly if they work only one or two sessions per week. Local NHS management's response to a practice's proposals to improve contractual arrangements may be very different from what is anticipated; in some circumstances management may decide to reduce the level of services in response to a demand for increased pay. In particular, GPs need to know that NHS trusts can choose to offer local contracts which differ from nationally negotiated agreements and do not necessarily contain the same safeguards in respect of job security or annual pay reviews.

GPs should obtain expert advice before raising any proposal with local hospital management. Otherwise they could find themselves unwittingly taking a precipitous or irrevocable step which prejudices their long-term position. In NHS trusts, GPs should also contact the local negotiating committee (LNC) which negotiates with trust management on behalf of medical staff.

How GPs are paid for hospital work

Clinical assistant grade

Even though the term 'clinical assistant' is not to be found anywhere in the hospital medical staff terms and conditions of service, this grade is nevertheless covered by the appointment procedures specified in paragraph 94 of these and also by NHS General Whitley Council agreements. When working as a clinical assistant, a GP should be responsible to a consultant and carry an overriding commitment to the hospital service rather than general practice. Thus GPs need to make arrangements to cover their practice obligations during those periods when working as clinical assistants.

Since 1988 the maximum number of notional half days for which a clinical assistant may be contracted is five, unless the doctor is an unrestricted GP principal, where the maximum is nine.

Clinical assistant posts are normally 12-month, fixed-term contracts and renewed annually. Any emergency and on-call duties should be spelt out clearly in the contract.

Box 8.1: Notional half day

Under paragraph 61 of the hospital terms and conditions of service a notional half day (i.e. session) is defined as three and a half hours, including travelling time.

Box 8.2: Key features of the clinical assistant grade

- travel expenses payable under certain conditions
- limited security of tenure
- study leave at employer's discretion
- pay related not to number of beds but to time commitment of job
- employee status
- no independent clinical responsibility
- no incremental pay scale

Hospital practitioner grade

Applicants for posts must be GP principals with:

- at least two years' full-time (or equivalent) hospital experience in a relevant specialty

OR

- a relevant specialist diploma and five years' experience as a clinical assistant

OR

- other equivalent experience.

Each post has to be advertised and its commitment cannot exceed five sessions per week. The qualifications and experience required of a

---

Box 8.3: Key features of the hospital practitioner grade

- study leave entitlement of 30 days in three years (pro rata)
- emergency and on-call duties should be specified in the contract
- hospital terms and conditions of service apply
- travel expenses paid in some circumstances
- security of tenure
- incremental pay scale
- no independent clinical responsibility

---

post-holder depend on both the post and the views of local consultants. Hospital practitioners do not have independent clinical responsibility and are therefore supervised by consultants. Hospital doctors' terms and conditions of service apply.

Staff fund arrangements

A staff fund is based on a local GP or community hospital and is made up of both bed fund payments and casualty payments. The distribution of payments (which are superannuable) from this fund is agreed among the local participating doctors attached to the hospital. Only GPs on the health authority list are appointed to a GP hospital under the bed fund arrangement, and they are free to organise for themselves how the work is undertaken. As independent clinicians they are accountable to their peers. The calculation of bed fund payments for inpatient GP beds is based on bed occupancy not time spent on the work.

Box 8.4: Key features of staff fund arrangements

- independent clinical responsibility – no consultant supervision
- doctor controls admission, management, administration and discharge
- no sick leave
- no study leave
- no annual leave
- no security of tenure
- no travel and other expenses
- very poorly paid

Casualty payments are paid into the bed fund and form part of it. The clinical assistant scale is used to calculate the size of these payments, but the payments as such are not connected to that grade. There are two kinds of payments: a retention fee and a fee which reflects the number of patient attendances. The fee based on attendance reflects the number of new patient attendances and the clinical assistant scale is normally used as an analogue for the rate of payments, though this may vary locally. Typically a given number of new attendances draws one clinical assistant session payment into the bed fund. Although the arrangements for casualty payments do not necessarily require GPs to see all patients when they first attend, each patient should be seen by a doctor at some stage. Nurses may treat minor problems, seeking advice and assistance from GPs as necessary. However, a GP must be available to attend immediately if required.

What a contract for hospital services should contain

The contract should state to which consultant the GP is clinically responsible. If supervised by a consultant, the post should normally be graded as either clinical assistant or hospital practitioner; the latter may be preferred because it has greater security of tenure and is more highly paid. Contracts for both grades should specify hours of work; however, it should be noted

---

Box 8.5: Contract checklist

The contract should include:

- name of employing authority
- date employment commences and any previous employment which may count towards continuity
- place of work
- job description
- hours of work
- superannuation
- remuneration
- annual leave
- study leave
- maternity leave
- sick leave
- definition of clinical responsibility
- substitution and deputising arrangements
- medical indemnity
- period of notice of termination
- disciplinary procedure
- grievance procedure
- reference to the terms and conditions of service for hospital medical and dental staff, as appropriate.

that although it is comparatively easy to calculate sessional payments for routine work it is usually more difficult to do so for out-of-hours work.

The hours during which casualty work is to be covered must be clearly specified; some GPs with surgeries on the same site as a GP hospital have found that between 9 am and 5 pm they receive no pay for casualty work because health authorities mistakenly consider it to be part of general medical services.

9 Flexible and part-time working in general practice

> **Where to obtain advice and assistance**
>
> BMA members can obtain expert advice and assistance on all contractual problems from their local BMA office. Health authorities are also an important source of advice. The BMA has published guidance on contracts for salaried GP assistants, which includes a model contract of employment.
>
> The BMA web site is at www.bma.org.uk
>
> Further reading includes Ellis N and Stanton T (eds) (1994) *Making Sense of Partnerships*. Radcliffe Medical Press, Oxford, and Ellis N and Chisholm J (1997) *Making Sense of the Red Book* (3e). Radcliffe Medical Press, Oxford.

The main opportunities for flexible and part-time working in general practice are:

- as a GP principal, particularly part-time and job-sharing GPs
- as a restricted services principal
- as a full- or part-time salaried employee – often termed an assistant
- as a member of the doctors' retainer scheme
- as an associate
- as a locum.

Although there are important statutory regulations and employment law governing these flexible and part-time arrangements, the actual contractual terms are matters to be agreed between the practice and the doctor. This latter point is important and needs to be stressed; much of the advice provided below is drawn from the BMA's recommendations relating to fair and reasonable contractual terms, but cannot be regarded as mandatory.

Part-time working as a GP principal

Five options of availability

The GP's terms of service provide five options of availability to patients. These arrangements do not alter a GP's basic responsibility to ensure that, either personally or through a deputy, general medical services are provided for patients throughout each and every day that his or her name is included on a health authority list.

Full time over five days

This option requires a GP to be normally available for not less than 26 hours spread over five days each week, for 42 weeks in any 12-month period.

Full time over four days

This second option allows a GP to be normally available for not less than 26 hours spread over four days each week for 42 weeks in any 12-month period. Doctors may apply for this option if they are involved in health-related activities, which are defined in the NHS regulations as those connected with:

- organisation of the medical profession or training of its members
- providing medical care or treatment
- improving quality of care or treatment
- administering general medical services, including working for a PCG/trust.

Health authorities should be guided by the illustrative list of these activities shown in Box 9.1.

Three-quarter time

A three-quarter-time contract allows a GP to be normally available for not less than 19 hours each week on days to be agreed with the health authority, for 42 weeks each year. This option is only available to principals in a partnership with at least one full-time partner.

Box 9.1: Health-related activities

- appointments concerned with medical education or training; for example, regional adviser, course organiser or an academic appointment
- medical appointments within the health service other than in relation to the provision of general medical services; for example, hospital appointments (such as hospital practitioner, clinical assistant and GP hospital posts) and also health service management and advisory posts, including health authority duties
- medical appointments made under the Crown, with government departments or agencies, or public or local authorities; for example, medical work for the police or prison service
- appointments concerning the regulation of the medical profession or the MPC; for example, General Medical Council (GMC) appointments, membership of the UK and national GPCs or the Royal College of General Practitioners (RCGP) at national level, or service on an LMC

Half-time

A half-time GP normally has to be available for not less than 13 hours each week on days to be agreed with the health authority, for 42 weeks each year. This option is only available to GPs in a partnership with at least one GP principal.

Job sharing

This enables a joint application by doctors in a partnership which includes both of them. Together they must be normally available for not less than 26 hours over five days each week for 42 weeks each year. The two doctors should decide how the 26 hours are to be divided.

Non-availability

Each of the above options requires the GP to be normally available for 42 weeks in any 12-month period. Throughout the 42 weeks but outside approved hours and during the remaining 10 weeks, a GP is free to make reasonable arrangement with a partner or a deputy for the care of patients.

Profit share and part-time partners

Under NHS regulations, for the health authority to recognise GPs as partners, it must be satisfied that they discharge the duties and exercise the powers of principals in the partnership and are entitled to a profit share based on one of the options in Box 9.2.

Each partnership must decide for itself how to run its business. But if any partner's share is grossly out of line with his or her contribution to the practice's workload, a concealed sale of goodwill may be deemed to have taken place.

Box 9.2: Minimum profit shares of part-timers

Full-time principals	minimum share is one third of that of partner with the greatest share
Three-quarter-time principals	minimum share is one quarter of that of partner with the greatest share
Half-time principals	minimum share is one fifth of that of partner with the greatest share
Job sharers	minimum joint share is one third of that of partner with greatest share

(These minimum profit shares apply only to the NHS component of the partnership profits. Income from work outside NHS general practice is excluded from the calculation.)

Discrimination

It is unlawful for a partnership of two or more partners to discriminate on grounds of sex or marital status, and for a partnership of six or more partners to discriminate on grounds of colour, race, nationality (including citizenship), or ethnic or national origins:

- when appointing a new partner
- in the terms on which the new partner is offered a partnership
- by refusing or deliberately neglecting to offer a partnership

and where someone is already a partner:

- in the way he or she is afforded access to any benefits, facilities or services
- by refusing or deliberately neglecting to afford access to those benefits, facilities and services
- by dismissing the partner or treating him or her unfavourably in any other way.

Maternity leave

As self-employed, independent contractors, women GP principals do not enjoy the employment rights relating to pregnancy and childbirth that apply to women employees. Thus partnerships are free to make their own arrangements for an individual partner's maternity leave. (*See* Box 9.3 for an outline of some recommended maternity leave arrangements for partnerships.)

There are various arrangements for paying locums employed during prolonged absences such as those arising from sickness or maternity leave.

Box 9.3: Recommended arrangements for maternity leave

- 18 weeks' absence should be regarded as a minimum entitlement and the pregnant partner should have the right to determine for herself when the period of absence should start, in consultation with her own GP
- the practice should consider the question of funding the cost of a locum to cover the actual workload of the pregnant partner, not merely her hours of availability
- the partnership should agree on a maximum period of absence following which a partner's failure to return to work may justify compulsory expulsion
- the exercise of a partner's right to maternity leave should not abolish her entitlement to pro rata holiday and sickness leave
- where this seems appropriate the partnership agreement should specify leave arrangements for adoption

A partnership agreement which provides for maternity leave on terms which are less advantageous than sick leave could be construed as evidence of indirect sex discrimination.

A simple method is for the absent partner to pay all the locum expenses. However, it is increasingly common for the first few weeks of locum expenses to be paid by the whole partnership.

A partnership will be infringing the Sex Discrimination Act 1976 if a pregnant partner is treated less favourably than a male partner with a distinctly male incapacity. Therefore a partner on maternity leave should not have to meet the full cost of a locum unless this arrangement also applies to sick leave.

A woman GP principal who provides unrestricted general medical services and is paid a basic practice allowance can claim additional payments for a locum actually engaged during absences due to pregnancy and childbirth. These payments are similar to those paid during sickness, but for maternity there are no list-size criteria. The payments are available for a maximum period of 18 weeks. These additional payments from the health authority should be paid to the absent partner if she is responsible for locum expenses. (Eligibility for additional payments during sickness depend on the average number of patients that the remaining GPs have to care for during the absence.)

The question of how long a partnership or individual partner pays locum expenses needs to be decided in relation to the arrangements for insurance cover for income protection and/or locum expenses.

Partnership agreements

As well as the minimum share of the profits referred to above, a doctor who is in partnership must discharge the duties and exercise the powers of a principal in the running of the partnership; irrespective of whether he or she is a part-time, job-sharing or full-time principal.

Working as a restricted services principal

The 'restricted services principal' provides general medical services which are limited to:

- child health surveillance services
- contraceptive services
- maternity medical services
- minor surgery services
- or any combination of these.

This is quite distinct from the 'restricted-list principal' who cares for a restricted category of patients connected with a particular establishment or organisation.

In general, a restricted services principal is eligible to receive only:

- those fees related to the particular service being provided
- discretionary payments under the rent and rates scheme and practice staff scheme.

Restricted principals providing maternity, contraceptive or child health surveillance services are also eligible to receive modified payments under the sickness and confinement schemes; but those providing only minor surgery services are not.

Doctors applying to become restricted principals for the minor surgery and child health surveillance lists will be approved only if they work either in a group with one or more principals or as an assistant or deputy of a principal who is on the relevant list. A restricted services principal must satisfy the specific criteria for entry to the relevant special list.

Working as a salaried GP or GP assistant

GP principals, whether single-handed or in a partnership, and Primary Care Act pilot schemes are all able to engage salaried GPs or assistants to help them provide patient services.

For GP principals the terms of service require that the health authority is informed when a salaried GP or assistant is being employed. GP principals are not allowed to employ one or more non-principal GPs for more than three months in any 12-month period without health authority consent, irrespective of whether that doctor's employment qualifies for payment of the assistant's allowance or for reimbursement under the practice staff scheme.

GP principals may employ other doctors at their own expense; they are eligible for additional payments (the assistant's allowance or reimbursement under the practice staff scheme) only if the criteria in Red Book paragraphs 18.1–18.6 or 52.1–52.37 are satisfied. The support that Primary Care Act pilot schemes can get for employing salaried GPs or assistants is a matter for negotiation with the health authority.

Salaried GPs and assistants should agree with their employing practices a written contract and job description. Every employer is required to issue a written statement of the main terms of employment to any employee within two months of starting work. For practices that claim reimbursement under the practice staff scheme for a salaried GP, it is a requirement that there is an agreed contract of employment to BMA standards.

Anyone considering working as a salaried GP or assistant may find the following checklist a helpful guide to those subjects which should be covered by an employment contract:

- pay, including provision for annual review
- hours of work, including any flexibility requirement
- holiday leave and pay entitlement
- sick leave and pay entitlement
- maternity leave and pay entitlement
- pensions arrangements
- notice of termination of contract
- grievance procedures
- arrangements for motoring expenses, medical defence organisation and other professional subscriptions.

In addition, there should be an agreed job description which describes the post's responsibilities and duties.

Pay for salaried GPs and assistants

It is not possible to specify a particular rate of pay or formula for determining pay which can suit all circumstances. Ultimately a salaried GP's pay should reflect the circumstances of the appointment; relevant factors include previous experience, hours of work, job content and the income of the practice. Two possible ways of determining a GP's salary are:

- a specific rate of pay, such as a salary which may be linked to some external comparator
- a formula which relates pay to the income of the practice.

Whichever is used, the actual salary must take account of both the employer's financial circumstances and the nature of the post itself.

The option of basing salary on a specific rate of pay has the advantage of simplicity (possible analogues include the NHS clinical assistant and hospital practitioner grades). The actual pay rate could take account of various factors including:

- previous experience
- hours of work

- out-of-hours commitment
- duties performed.

Some practices may wish to use a fairly complex formula to calculate relative workloads of both partners and salaried GPs or assistants.

The other option, where salary is based on a percentage of practice profits, also needs to take account of the factors listed above. It is hard to specify a percentage of parity to suit all circumstances; the GPC has suggested that a minimum 70–75% of parity should be a fair basis for calculating the salary for a full-time GP who does the whole range of general medical service duties (including the practice's out-of-hours commitment) but does not share the managerial responsibilities of the employing partners.

The GP retainer scheme

The scheme helps doctors who can only work a few days a week to keep in touch with general practice so that they can return to the NHS when circumstances permit. They are offered the opportunity of doing a small amount of paid professional work and to attend postgraduate medical education sessions; in return, scheme members are paid a retainer to help meet expenses. Some 1000 GPs are now in the scheme, following its revision in 1999.

A doctor joining the scheme agrees to:

- maintain GMC registration and membership of a medical defence organisation
- attend at least 25 hours of educational courses a year, which may be arranged to fit in with family responsibilities
- take a professional journal such as the *British Medical Journal*
- work at least one session a week and be prepared to take on more work, up to an average of four sessions a week if this does not interfere with family commitments.

How the scheme is organised

Health authorities have been responsible for the general administration of the scheme; they accept new members and pay the annual retainer fee. Professional advice and guidance about educational facilities are provided by the directors of postgraduate general practice education (DPGPEs) who should discuss career prospects with scheme members and advise them on local postgraduate activities, and review progress with scheme members at least annually. Educational sessions attended by members should be relevant to their current work and their eventual return to regular practice.

Scheme members can also do a limited amount of non-general medical services, e.g. family planning, such to the DPGPE's approval.

The employer is responsible for arranging and paying for work done. Membership is on a year-by-year basis and continues automatically for a maximum of five years.

The GPC has published a model contract of employment for retainees in general practice. As employees of a practice, retainees are entitled to join the NHS superannuation scheme.

The retainer fee and income tax

The retainer fee should be treated as earned income and taxed under Schedule E. After deducting allowable expenses the remaining balance will attract any personal income tax relief to which the doctor is entitled; these expenses are those incurred wholly, exclusively and necessarily in the performance of professional duties; for example, the annual GMC retention fee and subscriptions to professional bodies, such as a medical defence organisation and the BMA. (Subscription rates to medical defence organisations and the BMA are reduced for doctors with this level of income.)

Other fees: superannuation and income tax

The fees paid by the practice for work done under the scheme are liable to income tax and class 1 NI contributions, and are superannuable if the retainee chooses to join or remain a member of the NHS superannuation scheme. If a doctor already has two or more years' service with the NHS Pension Scheme his or her accrued benefits can be preserved. If total service is less than this, these benefits may be lost after a 12-month break in service; the doctor can prevent this by working at least one day in each 12-month period in superannuable employment. Alternatively, if none of the work undertaken in connection with the scheme is superannuable (e.g. working as a GP assistant), a doctor may apply to the NHS Pensions Agency at the Department of Health, 200–220 Broadway, Fleetwood, Lancs FY7 8LG, for employment under the scheme to be 'approved' for superannuation purposes, in order to avoid incurring a disqualifying break in service of 12 months or more.

Working as an associate

The associate scheme enables single-handed, isolated GPs to employ an associate. This allows them regular time off and training, in circumstances where continuous duty is an otherwise inescapable feature of their practice. Normally an associate is employed by two practices; although three may sometimes be appropriate. (GPs with assistants are ineligible for the scheme.)

Those GPs who participate in this scheme, and are also paid inducement payments, are no longer entitled to claim locum expenses, other than in the most exceptional circumstances.

Box 9.4 explains how the scheme has been modified to take account of the special geographical circumstances of remote areas of Scotland. To qualify for this allowance a GP must be single-handed (including job sharers) and:

- in receipt of rural practice payments

OR

- the sole practitioner on an island

AND ALSO

- in receipt of an inducement payment

Box 9.4: Special Scottish circumstances

Particular geographical difficulties, especially in the Highlands and Islands, may mean that it is impractical for two or three neighbouring principals to employ an associate. In these circumstances, health boards can organise a scheme if asked to do so by GPs.

GPs in very isolated areas, where groupings of two or three eligible principals are difficult if not impossible to arrange, can ask their health board to act as the paying agent on their behalf and to employ a suitably qualified associate. Though the board appoints, pays and deploys these associates, responsibility for them under the terms of service remains with the principal. In these circumstances, where the board acts solely as the agent, GPs should ensure that they are adequately represented on the selection panel appointed by the board to recruit associates.

OR

- practising more than 10 miles (measured along the most practicable route) from the nearest GP's main surgery or nearest district general hospital.

Doctors employed as associates must satisfy vocational training regulations and be eligible to apply to join a health authority list, but while holding this appointment must not be included on such a list.

Associates undertake all GP work and their employing GPs are responsible for their actions, including any breach of the terms of service. The associate scheme is broadly similar to the GP registrar scheme; the associate doctor has the same contractual relationship with the GP employer, the same accountability arrangements and the same tax status as a registrar does.

Because a GP principal is accountable for the activities of an associate, he or she should employ someone with the necessary skills and aptitude to be able to practise in social and professional isolation. This scheme may become a step in the career structure, offering a route to obtaining an isolated or inducement practice. A short-term 'apprenticeship' as an associate can enable a younger doctor to assess his or her own suitability for this type of practice.

The employing practice decides the associate's salary, but the amount reimbursed directly by the health authority will be on the associate scale of payments as set annually by the Review Body. Other reimbursements include a car allowance, telephone expenses, removal expenses, the cost of medical defence organisation subscriptions, the employer's NI contributions and other expenses similar to those covered by the GP registrar scheme. An associate may receive the postgraduate education allowance and time spent as an associate will count towards seniority payments in the same way as for GP assistants. Where two or three GPs jointly employ an associate, one of them has to be responsible to the health authority for administering salary, allowances and tax deductions.

The health authority has to be satisfied that the arrangements ensure continuity of care for patients, equitable and regular time off for both the GPs and the associate, that they cover the annual and postgraduate study leave, and that the associate is employed on a full-time basis. (In England and Wales the health authority can ask to see the associate's contract of employment.)

What an associate does

It is for the employing doctors to determine how an associate is deployed between the participating practices. However, doctors in isolated areas often have small lists of a few hundred patients so it is inappropriate for a principal to use the associate as simply an extra pair of hands; it is not the practice's workload that should need relieving but the unremitting on-call commitment. Most participating GPs will wish to be relieved of their practice responsibilities on a regular basis (probably for at least a week at a time) to compensate for the difficulties of ferry travel or long road journeys when leaving the practice area for a worthwhile break. At other times (e.g. school holidays) it should be possible to arrange a sustained break while staying in their own area knowing that time with their families will not be disrupted by practice commitments. It should be remembered that any practice arrangements will be subject to disruption in the event of sickness or maternity leave involving either practitioner or associate. When this occurs, balancing periods of leave or extra duty may be required to ensure equity.

Working as a locum

Locums in general practice can work long term or short term, part time or full time to cover, for example, a GP's absence on maternity or study leave, extended leave of absence or illness, or to cover a period before a new partner is appointed. Terms of employment vary, as does the existence of a contract of employment. Some locums also work for deputising services on a sessional basis.

Doctors may find locum employment advantageous, say, following vocational training when they may want experience in various practices before becoming a principal. Disadvantages may include poor job satisfaction, especially when there is no opportunity for continuity of patient care, lack of a proper contract of employment, poor pay and inadequate continuing medical education. Only long-term locums are eligible to claim Section 63 expenses for travel and subsistence to attend educational courses. Expenses are not normally reimbursed for locums on short-term contracts. The BMA can advise members on appropriate fees for locum work.

10 Part-time medical work outside the NHS

Although there are no official data on the amount of non-NHS work GPs undertake, unpublished data and anecdotal evidence suggest that the totality of GPs' earnings from this source amounts on average to barely 1 or 2% of their gross NHS income. Thus the total amount of these earnings is probably much smaller than is generally assumed. The extent of this work within general practice is often overestimated, because a small minority of practices who are heavily and enthusiastically involved in it have given wide publicity to its considerable potential income.

The main sources of GP earnings outside the NHS are:

- a wide range of miscellaneous fees paid for various part-time medical services

- private general practice
- work in occupational health.

Non-NHS medical work

GPs may charge fees for a range of non-NHS work, including fees for local or central government work, reports or certificates for their patients or third parties, and private treatment. Nevertheless, it needs to be remembered that GPs are prohibited by their NHS contracts from charging fees in certain specific circumstances (*see* Box 3.9, Chapter 3).

The level of fees that may be charged depends on whom the work is being carried out for and how the level is determined. The BMA divides these fees into four main categories (designated A, B, C and D) according to how they are determined (*see* Box 10.1).

Box 10.1: BMA categories of fees

Category A	fees prescribed by statute
Category B	fees negotiated nationally by the BMA with government departments, local authorities and other employers
Category C	fees negotiated nationally with representative bodies
Category D	fees suggested by the BMA

The BMA publishes 12 fees guidance schedules (*see* Box 10.2) which describe the level of fees applying to a particular area of work and the circumstances in which they may be paid; these cover several hundred individual fees and help to ensure GPs are paid correctly for their non-NHS services. The fees guidance schedules are available to BMA members only, free of charge, from their local BMA office.

The BMA considers that if an official body commissions a medical examination, report or certificate for which a GP may charge a fee, it should be liable for meeting the costs.

> **Box 10.2: Fees guidance schedules**
>
> The following fees guidance schedules are available separately from local BMA offices:
>
> | | |
> |---|---|
> | FGS1 | Central government departments and agencies |
> | FGS2 | Work for local authorities |
> | FGS3 | Miscellaneous work in the NHS |
> | FGS4 | Family planning |
> | FGS5 | Work for insurance companies |
> | FGS6 | Charitable societies |
> | FGS7 | Road accidents: emergency treatment |
> | FGS8 | Police work |
> | FGS9 | Work for coroners and crematoria |
> | FGS10 | Medico-legal fees |
> | FGS11 | Where no agreement applies |
> | FGS12 | Fees for GP non-principals |

Category A: statutory fees

A typical example is the fee for providing emergency treatment at road traffic accidents. These fees are always paid strictly according to the conditions stipulated in the relevant legislation. Box 10.3 lists the main types of fees in this category.

> **Box 10.3: Category A: statutory fees and fees determined by government departments**
>
> - fees for blood tests and reports relating to evidence of paternity
> - allowances paid by the Crown Prosecution Service and the Lord Chancellor's Department to witnesses in criminal cases for both written medical reports and attendance at court (FGS10)
> - emergency treatment following road traffic accidents (FGS7)
> - examinations under the Factories Acts and health and safety at work legislation
> - medical examinations required under the diving regulations
> - aviation medical fees
> - dental anaesthetic fees
> - seafarers' statutory medical examinations

Category B: fees negotiated with central government departments and public sector employers

These are traditionally linked to Review Body recommendations; typical examples include fees for part-time services to certain government departments, local authorities and police authorities. They are paid by the government department or employer which negotiated the fee. Box 10.4 summarises the main fees in this category. At the time of writing the profession is in dispute with various government departments because they have deliberately breached an agreement to increase these fees.

Box 10.4: Category B: work for central government departments

Range of fees for various procedures including:

- medical examinations and reports
- medical attendance on non-NHS patients
- regular attendance at government establishments

Employment Service Division

- disablement advisory committees panels

Department of Transport

- extract from medical records or completing DVLA questionnaires
- DVLA diagnostic tests

DSS

- fees for various reports required for pension and other purposes
- part-time referee for the Benefits Agency medical service
- membership of various tribunals

HSE

- extracts from records plus opinion

Home Office (Prison Service)

- part-time prison medical officers (agreed directly with the Home Office Prison Service)

Category C: fees negotiated with representative organisations

Typical examples are fees for life assurance reports, and work for voluntary and charitable societies. The BMA's negotiated fees apply to only those organisations which are members of the national representative body; for example, life assurance report fees are only binding on member companies of the Association of British Insurers. Box 10.5 lists the main fees in this category.

Box 10.5: Category C: fees negotiated with representative organisations

- fees for life assurance reports (FGS5)
- voluntary aid societies (e.g. British Red Cross Society, St John Ambulance Association) (FGS6)

Category D: suggested fees

This category includes all those fees not determined by negotiation or statute; they are left to be agreed between the GP and the party concerned. The extensive list of the many and varied types in Box 10.6 is provided as

---

Box 10.6: Category D: fees suggested by the BMA for various types of private work

(Most of these fees are covered by FGS11)

- holiday insurance certificate
- blood test (not involving disputed paternity)
- cervical cytology (non-NHS)
- private medical consultations
- copying medical notes
- comprehensive medical examinations and reports
- fitness to attend court as a witness
- cremation forms B and C
- removal of a pacemaker following death
- pre-employment examinations

Box 10.6: *continued*

- reports requested by employers
- private sickness absence certificates for school or work
- motor insurance certificates of fitness
- accident and sickness insurance certificates
- validation of provident association claim form
- school fees insurance
- fitness for higher education
- fitness to participate in a sport
- freedom from infection certificate
- vaccination and immunisation
- attendances at police stations not covered by NHS fee at patient's request
- family planning
- lecture fees
- non-NHS minor surgery
- seatbelt exemption certificates
- prescriptions for drugs required in overseas travel
- reports for drug companies
- race meetings and sporting activities
- private nursing homes
- data protection legislation: search of records
- access to medical records: copying fee
- reports on prospective subscribers to health insurance
- passport and photocard driving licence signing
- payments to deputising doctors
- fees for involvement in legal work (i.e. professional witnesses and expert witnesses where legal aid does not apply)

a reminder of private services for which GPs may charge patients. GPs are often reticent about charging NHS patients for non-NHS services and patients are correspondingly reluctant to pay for them. In a publicly funded service which is still permeated by the non-pecuniary ethos, GPs and patients are unaccustomed to monetary transactions. Each practice will obviously determine its own policy on charging patients for this work; a determined effort may have to be made to overcome any inhibitions about introducing the cash nexus into patient–doctor relations, and to inform patients of which NHS services they can legitimately expect to receive free of charge and for which non-NHS services they can properly be charged.

Deciding what to charge

GPs should clarify whether they are entitled to charge a fee before agreeing to provide a service. If it is clear that a fee may be charged, the next question that has to be answered is for whom is the medical service being provided. This is crucial because the answer determines both the level of fee and who should pay it. Whether or not a fee may be charged is determined by either statute or the GP's terms of service. It is advisable to forewarn patients of any charge before undertaking the work. Hopefully this should avoid some of the embarrassment that can arise in NHS general practice when charges are being made for non-NHS services. Some practices find it helpful to have a notice about this in the waiting room.

GPs are obliged under paragraph 13 of their terms of service to provide patients with 'all necessary and appropriate personal medical services of the type usually provided by general practitioners' for which they are not permitted to ask, or accept, any payment (*see* paragraph 37) except if this is specifically allowed in the terms of service (*see* paragraph 38). A full list of services for which an NHS patient may be charged is given in Box 3.9 (Chapter 3). Although some certificates may be charged for, NHS GPs are obliged under the terms of service to provide the certificates specified in Box 3.9 (Chapter 3) free of charge, including those supporting social security benefit claims. GPs in Primary Care Act pilot schemes are similarly constrained.

Private general practice

There is no limit on the amount of private practice NHS GPs may undertake provided they fulfil their NHS commitment. If staff or premises, which are directly reimbursed for NHS purposes, are used and a practice's private practice income is more than 10% of total practice receipts, these NHS reimbursements will be proportionally abated. Under no circumstances, except those referred to above which are permitted under their terms of service, can GPs charge a fee to their own NHS patients.

The actual amount of private practice undertaken by NHS GPs as a whole is very small; only a small minority of practices are likely to have a

---

Box 10.7: Services for which fees may not be charged

Death certificates

In England and Wales, the registered medical practitioner who was in attendance on the deceased during his or her last illness must deliver a death certificate, stating to the best of his or her knowledge and belief, the cause of death to the local registrar forthwith, and he or she may not charge a fee for this service. Failure to deliver the certificate 'without reasonable excuse' is punishable on summary conviction with a fine. He or she must also hand the person designated as 'qualified informant' the outer detachable part of the certificate form entitled 'Notice to Informant', duly completed.

Stillbirth certificates

Any registered medical practitioner who was present at the birth or examined the body of a stillborn child must, on a request from the 'qualified informant', give a certificate stating that the child was not born alive, and, where possible, stating to the best of his or her knowledge and belief the cause of death and estimated duration of the pregnancy.

**GPs under contract to health authorities
(health board in Scotland)**

The items for which doctors may not make charges are listed in Schedule 2 (term of service for doctors) of the NHS (General Medical Services) Regulations 1992 (Statutory Instrument No 635) as amended. In Scotland they are listed in Schedule 1 of The NHS (General Medical and Pharmaceutical Services) (Scotland) Regulations 1974 (Statutory Instrument No 506) as amended. Subsequent amendments are incorporated into the following:

(i)   England and Wales   paragraphs 38–42 of the England and Wales Schedule

(ii) Scotland   paragraph 20 of the Scottish Schedule.

---

significant number of private patients. Typically NHS GPs accept private patients only on request; they do not advertise for patients, though they are now free to do so subject to the guidance laid down by the General Medical Council.

An NHS GP cannot treat a patient both privately and on the NHS concurrently. This is because all NHS GPs are prohibited from accepting any payment from patients for whose treatment they are responsible under their NHS contract, unless such payments are specifically authorised. This restriction on receiving payments extends to patients registered with the GP's partners. Some patients have both an NHS GP and a private GP from a different practice.

A private GP may agree to be 'on call' for private patients but is not obliged to do so unless the contract with the patient specifically includes an out-of-hours service. The NHS out-of-hours contractual obligation does not apply to the private sector.

NHS GPs must only provide an NHS prescription (FP10) to their NHS patients; they cannot prescribe an NHS prescription for private patients.

Many NHS GPs treat their private patients on the same or a similar basis to their NHS patients; both surgery and domiciliary consultations are arranged to fit in with their NHS commitments.

Private general practice is based on a personal contract between the doctor and patient. For some years the provident associations have not shown any interest in offering insurance schemes to cover the costs of private general practice, although some insurance companies have recently expressed an interest in such policies.

There is one aspect of general practice which merits further clarification, namely the treatment of overseas visitors. A Health Department circular which governs these matter states that, apart from immediately necessary (i.e. emergency) treatment, the NHS GP has unrestricted discretion as to whether to treat a non-EU visitor as a temporary resident and NHS patient, or as a wholly private patient. The health circular makes it clear that many non-EU visitors expect to pay for medical treatment and GPs will not be committing any offence or breach of their terms of service if they offer to treat them privately on whatever terms are mutually agreed. However, most visitors from other EU countries have some entitlement under EU regulations to use the NHS, including GP services. Their entitlement varies according to their employment and/or visitor status. For most purposes it is best to assume they (together with nationals from non-EU or European Economic Area states who have signed the European Social Charter) are entitled to free NHS treatment, except in the case of treatment which they have specifically come to the UK to obtain.

The circular also states that if no local NHS GP is willing to treat the non-EU visitor on an NHS basis, he or she can apply to the health authority to be assigned to the list of a local GP. The GP to whom the patient is assigned is obliged to provide NHS general medical services free of charge for the minimum number of days as specified in the NHS terms of service. There is, however, a major difference between primary and secondary care. Even if an overseas visitor receives NHS general medical services, access to NHS secondary care entirely depends on residency status and country of origin.

Occupational health

Although many doctors working in this specialty hold full-time salaried posts in large commercial and industrial organisations, there are also many part-time occupational physicians, most of whom are GPs. Some small firms prefer to employ a local doctor on a part-time sessional basis and GPs are ideally suited to fill these posts, although many firms have no occupational health service at all.

The BMA's Occupational Health Committee publishes suggested salary ranges for full- and part-time occupational physician posts and annualised salaries based on one hour, two hours or one session (three and a half hours) per week. These scales are included in a BMA booklet, *The Occupational Physician*, which also provides guidance on managing occupational health departments, and notes on health and safety in the workplace. These scales take account of the doctor's qualifications in occupational medicine (e.g. AFOM or DIH), previous relevant experience and level of responsibility. Thus GPs who are members or fellows of the Faculty of Occupational Medicine and are accredited specialists and/or have considerable experience should start at relatively higher salaries. The scales are based on the assumption that the GP does not benefit from paid annual leave or membership of the firm's superannuation scheme.

An occupational physician is in a somewhat unusual position in relation to the organisation's workforce in that there may be a danger that the normal rules governing medical ethics and confidentiality conflict with his or her responsibility to the organisation's management. Guidance on how to handle these potentially conflicting responsibilities is provided in two BMA publications, *The Occupational Physician* and *Medical Ethics Today: its philosophy and practice*.

Police surgeon work

The remuneration of police surgeons (which is classified as category B work) consists of a basic retainer fee which is partly based on experience and qualifications, and a two-tier item-of-service fee depending on the

---

**Box 10.8: The duties of an occupational physician
are of two main kinds:**

- assessing and moderating the effects of health on an individual's capacity to work, including:
  - advising employers on such matters as pre-employment and annual medical examinations
  - immediately treating clinical emergencies at the place of work
  - examining and monitoring employees returning to work after prolonged sickness absence
  - advising management on health surveillance and screening
- assessing and moderating the effects of work on an individual's health, which includes:
  - providing first aid services
  - examining and supervising medically those employees exposed to special hazards
  - advising management on the working environment, health risks, safety hazards and statutory requirements relating to health and safety at the workplace
  - supervising the hygiene of staff facilities, especially kitchens, canteens, etc.
  - educating the staff on matters pertaining to health, fitness and hygiene

---

type of case. Sexual assault and child abuse cases attract a higher fee. The fee for the first case is in all types of cases higher than for subsqent cases on the same call-out. These item-of-service fees are also payable if a doctor who is not a contracted police surgeon agrees to undertake the police visit. The fees are jointly negotiated by the BMA and the local government employers' organisation and apply throughout Great Britain.

The 'availability fee' is a flat-rate payment and not dependent on fee income. It may be supplemented by a further payment if the doctor has a relevant qualification (e.g. the diploma of medical jurisprudence or some other recognised qualification in forensic medicine) or has had 15 years' continuous service as a police surgeon (or deputy), normally with the same police force.

The item-of-service fees are paid when a doctor attends in response to a call from the police; they vary according to:

- when the call-out occurred

- length of time involved
- type of work undertaken
- whether a full written report or statement is required.

The work itself involves a varied range of duties, including:

- attending a police station to examine a prisoner, victim or police officer in relation to a wide variety of criminal offences
- attending a scene of unexpected death to advise the police
- attending a court as a witness.

Future prospects

Radical changes in the way in which government departments contract for part-time medical services are in the offing, and these are creating a climate of uncertainty among GPs (and other doctors) who have traditionally undertaken this work. The life assurance industry is also reviewing its methods of assessing risks and questioning the value of the medical examination and report.

There are no signs of any general expansion in the demand for private general practice. Like other activities, this is affected by the economic climate and its prevalence is strongly influenced by specific local socioeconomic and cultural factors. It is heavily concentrated in particular localities where there is a predominance of foreign residents and patients with high disposable incomes.

The prospects for non-NHS part-time work for GPs are not favourable. The current economic climate has taken its toll on the opportunities for work in occupational medicine by bringing in its wake contractions and closures among many small businesses. Other firms have merged and rationalised their arrangements for occupational health medicine. However, more extensive and stringent health and safety laws may generate some expansion in this work.

11 Practice accounts

The majority of GPs work in partnerships and almost all new GP principals enter general practice by joining an existing partnership. This chapter concentrates on the basic principles of accounting as they apply to partnerships. However, the basic accounting principles and methodology described below obviously apply equally to single-handed practitioners.

Partnership accounts provide a crucial record of a practice's profit for the accounting year and also show its financial worth at the balance sheet date. They also provide the basis for the completion of the Self Assessment Tax Return or Partnership Tax Return to be submitted to the Inland Revenue to calculate the income tax liability. Most importantly, the accounts should enable partners to review their practice's performance and plan its future development. They must, therefore, summarise clearly and concisely the practice's income and expenses and its net worth, and provide enough information to analyse its performance, including making comparisons with GPs' intended average gross and average net remuneration.

Accounting policies

These should be clearly set out in a statement attached to the practice accounts and would normally include the following:

- accounts have been prepared under the historical cost convention
- accounts have been prepared on the accruals basis so as to reflect annual income earned and expenditure incurred during the year
- definition of income receivable
- stock has been valued at the lower of cost and net realisable value
- method and rates of depreciation calculation used to write down the cost of fixed assets over their expected useful lives.

Furthermore, for the accounting period ended on 6 April 1999 or later, the Inland Revenue has said that the profits or losses as disclosed in the annual Partnership Tax Return should be on the basis of 'true and fair' criteria.

'True and fair' is defined in the Financial Reporting Standard for Smaller Entities (FRSSE), which has previously applied only to limited companies but in the eyes of the Inland Revenue should be applied to unincorporated businesses.

The income and expenditure account

This summarises income – including investment income – and expenditure for the year. It is helpful to include the previous year's figures as comparatives so that partners can readily compare these with this year's performance. The following principles should be followed when preparing partnership accounts.

The grossing-up principle

As the Review Body pay award takes account of the level of expenses shown in GPs' accounts, together with personal claims for expenses and business interest relief included in their tax returns, it is important that all expenses are shown gross in the accounts. The Statement of Fees and Allowances (the Red Book) advises that all income and expenses should be shown gross in the accounts, and that, for example, staff costs should not be netted off against staff reimbursements, or premises costs against rent and rates reimbursements.

The accruals basis

The income and expenditure account should be prepared on an accruals basis, i.e. in a way which reflects actual income earned and expenditure incurred during the accounting period, rather than simply cash paid and received. This is particularly relevant to any partnership where there has been a change of partners or profit shares; in these circumstances it is essential that all income earned and expenditure incurred by the partners in the year is allocated between them in that year's accounts. The term 'debtors' refers to the amount of money due to the practice at the balance sheet date; this consists mainly of health authority payments due to the practice at the end of the accounting year. For example, if the accounting year ends on 30 June, any fees and allowances received in the September quarter payment, which nevertheless relate to money earned during the June quarter, should be included as debtors.

If the accruals basis is not adopted then it will be necessary to make an adjustment in the tax return to convert the profit disclosed to this basis in respect of accounting dates ending on 6 April 1999 or later.

Valuing drugs

A stock-take needs to be made at the end of the accounting year of all drugs held by the practice. These should be valued at either cost or net realisable value, whichever is lower. Their value should be included on the balance sheet as an asset, being a part of the practice's net worth. Thus, if a partner retires from the practice, he or she has a share in the practice's stock of drugs, as valued at the end of the accounting year, or such retirement date. Record of the stock valuation must be retained.

Depreciation

This charge is included in the income and expenditure account to enable the original cost of an asset to be spread over its useful life. The appropriate proportion of the original cost of an asset should be included in the expenses for each year, rather than reducing the profit of the year by the whole amount of its original cost. The partners (on the advice of their accountants) should decide which depreciation rates to apply to their assets. Once these have been decided they should be applied consistently. The following depreciation rates are commonly used:

- computer equipment $33\frac{1}{3}\%$ per annum
- medical equipment   20% per annum

- furniture and fittings   10–15% per annum
- office equipment   15–20% per annum
- motor cars   25% per annum
- surgery premises   not normally depreciated.

Since practices, or their accountants, can choose their own depreciation rates, the Inland Revenue does not give tax relief on the amount of depreciation included in the accounts. Instead, it allows tax relief on the purchase of fixed assets by means of standardised capital allowances.

Allocating profits to partners

When the profit for the accounting period has been calculated, it is then distributed among the partners according to the practice's profit-sharing arrangements. If there are no changes in either the partnership or its profit-sharing ratios during the year, this should be a comparatively straightforward exercise. However, if such changes have occurred, it is necessary to allocate the profit by reference to the various profit-sharing periods. This may be done by attempting to allocate it accurately between different profit-sharing periods, such that income earned and expenditure incurred in these periods is identified and attributed to the relevant periods. Subject to the detail and quality of accounting records maintained, this may be time-consuming and, consequently, expensive to do. Alternatively, profits may be apportioned on a time basis, which means that if a new partner is admitted half-way through a year, half of the profits would be allocated to the first period and half to the second. This is the most popular method of distributing profits.

Obviously if the appointment or retirement of a partner is likely to affect significantly the practice's profitability, it may be advisable to apportion the income on a best estimate of the actual basis. However, because it is often extremely difficult to allocate expenses on a strictly actual basis, it may be fairer (and certainly much simpler) to apportion expenses on a time basis.

In principle, all items of practice income and expenditure must be included in the accounts so that the profit accurately reflects what is actually being generated by the practice. However, some practices have agreed that not all income should be shared among the partners according to their profit-sharing ratios. Instead, income from sources such as seniority awards, night consultations, out-of-hours rota fees and postgraduate education allowance may be retained on a personal basis by individual partners. According to this arrangement, such income should be regarded as prior shares of profit and, therefore, allocated to partners before the resulting balance is divided between them according to the agreed profit-sharing ratios. Similarly, if not all partners own the premises, or partners own the premises in different ratios to those applying to profit shares, income and expenditure relating to ownership of the surgery should be allocated as a prior share among property-owning partners according to the ratios in which they own the premises. The net surgery income comprises health authority rent allowances less interest on partnership loans relating to the premises, and any other expenditure which it is agreed should be borne by the property-owning partners.

Capital grants

If health authority improvement grants and fundholding management allowances are paid to a practice as a contribution towards its capital expenditure, these should be offset in the accounts against the cost of relevant assets so that only the net cost is depreciated and included in the balance sheet.

Health authority improvement grant payments and fundholding management allowances need to be shown separately; although capital allowances may be claimed if a management allowance is paid, these cannot be claimed if an improvement grant is paid towards the cost of an asset. Any claim is additionally restricted to the net cost after reimbursement of the asset. Of course fundholding was abolished in England, Scotland and Wales on 31 March 1999 and will be on 31 March 2000 in Northern Inland.

Presenting the accounts

Figure 11.1 shows an example of how to lay out income and expenditure accounts for a GP practice and how to allocate profits among partners. The accounts refer partners to more detailed information so that they can analyse the practice's performance. The various NHS fees and allowances received by the practice are shown in Figure 11.2.

The practice's income consists of four main elements: allowances, capitation payments, sessional payments and item-of-service fees. On average, a GP's income is distributed among these as follows:

	%
• allowances	18
• capitation payments	62

cont. on p. 127

DRS SMITH & PARTNERS
INCOME AND EXPENDITURE ACCOUNT
YEAR ENDED 30 JUNE 1999

	1999		1998	
	£	£	£	£
Income				
National Health Service fees	282 796		251 479	
Reimbursements	152 716		143 374	
Appointments	15 500		14 900	
Other income	45 168		23 804	
Fundholding management allowance	24 500		32 600	
Total income		520 680		466 157
Expenditure				
Practice expenses	35 628		34 715	
Premises expenses	23 281		20 784	
Staff expenses	149 320		139 712	
Administration expenses	22 438		21 155	
Finance expenses	23 264		23 404	
Depreciation	3745		3518	
Fundholding expenses	24 500		32 600	
Total expenditure		282 176		275 888
		238 504		190 269
Investment income				
Bank interest receivable	200		130	
Building society interest receivable	160		170	
		360		300
Net profit for the year		238 864		190 569

Allocation of profits

	Prior shares £	Share of balance £	Total £	Total £
Dr Smith	9103	54 693	63 796	50 197
Dr Patel	7224	54 693	61 917	49 630
Dr Green	7312	54 693	62 005	48 431
Dr Jones	18 329	32 817	51 146	42 311
	41 968	196 896	238 864	190 569

Figure 11.1 A sample income and expenditure account, showing allocation of profits

National Health Service fees	1999 £	1998 £
Allowances		
Practice allowances	30 048	24 868
Seniority awards	2901	898
Postgraduate education allowances	9480	7815
Rural practice payments	–	–
Trainee supervision grant	–	–
Out-of-hours annual payment	8965	7181
	51 124	40 762
Capitation payments		
Capitation fees	139 778	127 006
Deprivation payments	19	8
Registration fees	12 086	9905
Child health surveillance	3287	3275
Target payments:		
Cervical cytology	8797	8110
Childhood immunisations	2266	2062
Pre-school boosters	6637	6654
	172 870	157 020
Sessional payments		
Health promotion payments	12 564	11 130
Minor surgery	5629	6342
Teaching medical students	–	–
	18 193	17 472
Item-of-service fees		
Night consultations	2518	2336
Temporary residents	2429	2316
Contraceptive services	19 704	14 249
Emergency treatment and INT	464	954
Maternity	5913	7544
Vaccinations and immunisations	4253	3747
	35 281	31 146
Special drugs	5328	5079
Total	282 796	251 479

Figure 11.2 Fees and allowances received by a practice

- sessional payments   6
- item-of-service payments   12
- special drugs   2

  Total   **100**

Practices should review how their income is distributed. A significant variation from the above pattern may point to areas where a practice can increase activity and income.

GP principals are self-employed individuals for tax purposes and enter into a contract for services with their health authorities. The Review Body's pay award sets the levels of various NHS fees and allowances for the year. It also determines the intended average gross remuneration and the element of that gross income which is deemed to cover indirect expenses, thereby arriving at a figure for intended average net remuneration. The intended gross and net income per principal as set by the Review Body are published in the medical press, and practices should compare their accounts with these intended average levels.

Direct reimbursement

In addition to receiving indirect reimbursements for general expenses through the generality of fees and allowances, GPs are also directly reimbursed for practice staff, surgery premises, computers, drugs, GP registrar salaries, staff training and certain locum fees. The allocation of some of these reimbursements will in future be determined by primary care groups or their equivalents. It is also possible in certain cases to claim an allowance for the employment of an assistant or retained doctor. It is important that these direct reimbursements are shown clearly in the accounts so that a practice can identify easily the real cost of various activities; for example, the real cost of taking on an additional member of staff is the total cost less any direct reimbursement. In general, it is essential that direct reimbursements are not netted out against expenditure, because this reduces the total amount of expenses reported to the Review Body to enable it to determine GPs' pay.

Accounting records

The information in the income and expenditure account is obtained by the practice's accountants from the practice's own accounting records. These should comprise a cash book, a petty cash book, payroll records and an analysis of health authority income. The latter should show all fees and allowances received from the health authority during the year, dividing them into the elements shown in Figure 11.2. This provides a vital record for the practice to monitor NHS income and quickly identify any fall below the expected level. Many of these accounting records may be computerised.

The balance sheet

This is a statement of the practice's financial position at the end of the accounting year. It is important to note that it is merely a snapshot of the amounts owed to and by the practice at a particular point in time. On the very next day cash may be received from a debtor, thereby increasing the amount shown as cash and reducing that shown as debtors, and in turn this cash may be used to pay a creditor. Such cash movements would not affect the practice's overall total net assets, although these will change during the following year as profit is earned and drawn by partners.

The balance sheet has two distinct purposes: first, to ascertain whether the assets of the practice are sufficient to cover its liabilities, and second, to calculate the value of the partners' investment in the practice.

It is important to recognise that the accounts being prepared are those of the business in its own right and not those of its owners, who are the partners. This is an important distinction; these have to be seen as separate entities if their relationship (which is clearly shown in the balance sheet) is to be properly understood. Partners invest their funds in the practice as a business and therefore the balance sheet shows in the capital and current accounts the amount of the funds due to the partners. Thus the balance sheet contains:

- assets
- liabilities
- partners' funds.

Accordingly, the net assets of the partnership, which comprise its assets less its liabilities, always equal the partners' funds; thus the two halves of the balance sheet should literally balance. Figure 11.3 shows how the balance sheet distinguishes between partners' funds and the use of these for different purposes. The various subheadings on the balance sheet are described below.

DRS SMITH & PARTNERS
BALANCE SHEET
30 JUNE 1999

	1999		1998	
	£	£	£	£
Fixed assets		381 610		370 906
Current assets				
Stock of drugs	1870		1650	
Debtors	31 921		28 102	
Balance at building society	35 170		31 900	
Cash at bank and in hand	8950		7211	
	77 911		68 863	
Current liabilities				
Bank overdraft	1024		–	
Creditors	11 450		10 215	
Due to former partner	603		3150	
	13 077		13 365	
Net current assets		64 834		55 498
		446 444		426 404
Financed by:				
Property capital accounts		87 416		80 716
Capital accounts		20 000		20 000
Current accounts		5361		5870
Taxation provision		43 100		40 105
		155 877		146 961
Long-term liabilities				
Mortgage loans		290 567		279 713
		446 444		426 404

Figure 11.3 Division of partners' funds

The difference between fixed and current assets

An asset may be defined as something owned by the business and available for its future use.

Fixed assets are those used by the business over a period of several years to help earn profits, but not actually available for resale. These are depreciated to spread their cost over their working life and to apportion the cost (as far as possible) appropriately among the relevant partners.

Conversely, current assets are acquired for sale and conversion into cash during the normal course of the practice's business; for example, dispensing drugs are acquired for resale to generate profit.

The term 'debtors' is used to describe monies owed to the practice for goods or services already provided which are convertible into cash, which is itself a current asset.

The difference between current and long-term liabilities

Current liabilities are amounts owed by the practice and payable within 12 months of the end of the accounting year. These include creditors, amounts due to former partners, capital repayments of a long-term loan due within the next 12 months and bank overdrafts, which are always repayable on demand!

Long-term liabilities are capital amounts outstanding on loans which are repayable over a period longer than 12 months.

The total obtained by subtracting liabilities from assets is the partnership's net assets; this figure represents the net worth of the business and is equal to the partners' funds, being their investment in the practice.

Partners' funds

It helps to understand the nature of their investment in the practice if the partners' funds are divided between long-term investments (which can only be withdrawn when they retire from the practice) and those amounts which reflect the difference between partners' profit shares for the year and their drawings from the practice. The latter represents the money which may be withdrawn from the practice when the accounts are finally agreed.

Thus the partners' funds should be divided into these categories:

- property capital accounts
- capital accounts
- current accounts
- taxation provisions.

Some practices may decide to merge the property capital and capital account balances into a combined capital account.

The property capital account

This is the partners' net equity in the premises and is the difference between the premises' cost or valuation and any outstanding partnership loans.

If the premises are funded by individual partners' personal loans rather than by a partnership loan, the property capital accounts should show the cost or value of the premises and the partners' borrowing will be shown 'off' balance sheet.

Capital accounts

The partners' capital accounts refer to the funds provided for working capital to enable the practice to run smoothly. The amount of this working capital varies between practices, reflecting the net book value of fixed assets (excluding premises) funded by the partners rather than by partnership loans, and also the value of debtors and creditors to a practice. The capital account therefore funds the purchase of fixed assets and the practice's day-to-day expenditure so that it can run without the risk of incurring an overdraft at times when income may be lower than expenditure.

Both the property capital and capital accounts should be established in the partners' agreed capital-sharing ratios as set out in the partnership agreement to ensure that capital funding is on an equitable basis. A partner's share of this capital will remain in the practice until he or she leaves the partnership.

Current accounts

These reflect the difference between partners' share of the profits for the year less the amounts they have withdrawn, superannuation payments, any sum earmarked for tax and any other personal payments made by the practice on behalf of the individual partners. Figure 11.4 shows the

Partners' current accounts

	Dr Smith £	Dr Patel £	Dr Green £	Dr Jones £	Total £
Balance at 1 July 1998	1811	1980	1965	114	5870
Profit for the year	63 796	61 917	62 005	51 146	238 864
Leave advances	1550	1550	1550	1550	6200
Cash introduced	–	–	–	5000	5000
Income tax repaid	510	–	–	–	510
	67 667	65 447	65 520	57 810	256 444
Monthly drawings	31 129	32 517	34 044	17 488	115 178
Fees retained privately	2300	1900	2150	6400	12 750
Payment of personal expenses	750	–	–	4800	5550
Spouses' salaries	1200	1200	1200	–	3600
Leave advances withdrawn	1550	1550	1550	1550	6200
Prior shares withdrawn	8353	5324	5162	11 929	30 768
Transfers to property capital accounts	1675	1675	1675	1675	6700
Transfers to tax provisions (*see* Figure 11.5)	10 150	9800	12 850	9150	41 950
PAYE on appointments	2900	2900	–	–	5800
Class 1 NIC	540	540	–	–	1080
Class 2 NIC	335	335	335	335	1340
Superannuation:					
Standard	3264	3264	3264	2785	12 577
Added years	–	680	–	–	680
Appointments	465	465	–	–	930
Leave advances repaid	1495	1495	1495	1495	5980
	66 106	63 645	63 725	57 607	251 083
Balance at 30 June 1999	1561	1802	1795	203	5361

Figure 11.4   Partners' current accounts

information which should be included to allow each partner to analyse changes in their current account during the year.

Leave advances are included in the current account if these are withdrawn by the partners. They are effectively interest-free loans repayable by deduction from the health authority's quarterly payments, and they therefore do not affect a practice's profit.

The current account balances at the annual accounting date should be in the partners' profit-sharing ratio. If not, then action should be taken to equalise them into this ratio over an agreed period of time.

Providing for tax liabilities

Since the introduction of the Self Assessment and current-year basis of assessment tax regime, income tax liabilities are no longer assessable on the partnership but on the individual. Consequently, practices may agree to save for the individual tax liabilities of the partners within the practice or for partners to save personally for their tax liabilities.

From a prudent point of view, a system of compulsory saving within the practice can be a very good discipline.

Making provision for tax payments is essentially a book-keeping exercise. Within the practice's accounts certain amounts are charged to each partner's current account and credited to a tax provision account in the same partner's name. Payments to the Inland Revenue are drawn from these tax provision accounts. This does not necessarily require the tax to be deposited in a separate bank or building society account; it simply retains the cash in the partnership by preventing partners from withdrawing it from their current accounts. This retained money can be used by the practice as working capital, particularly since it is comparatively easy to plan in advance for its payment to the Inland Revenue.

This arrangement has the advantage of ensuring that each partner's tax liabilities have been provided for. So long as partners' drawings are calculated on a 'net of tax' basis, there should always be enough funds in the tax provision accounts to meet a partner's tax liability.

To illustrate this, the amount of tax provision in accounts for the year ended 30 June 1999 should be sufficient to cover the whole of the 1999/2000 liability.

Figure 11.5 illustrates a partnership taxation provision, and movements within the individual partners' tax provision accounts are shown in Figure 11.6.

Partnership taxation provision

Provision has been made in the accounts for income tax and Class 4 NIC liabilities based on profits up to 30 June 1999.

	£
1998/99	10 450
1999/2000	40 345
Less overlap relief	(7695)
	43 100

The provision at 1 July 1998 consisted of:

	£
1997/98	16 046
1998/99	20 900
Less overlap relief	(7695)
	29 251

Figure 11.5 A partnership tax provision based on each individual partners' liability

Fundholding and partnership accounts

Fundholding was abolished in England, Wales and Scotland on 31 March 1999 and is to be abolished in Northern Ireland on 31 March 2000.

Fundholders have to produce a separate account for their fundholding activities and these must be drawn up to 31 March each year, regardless of the accounting year of the main practice account. However, there is some interaction between the fundholding and main practice accounts.

The management allowance

This is paid to a practice to cover fundholding management expenses. Thus, in both the preparatory year and the fundholding years, the allowance

Movements on taxation provision

	Dr Smith £	Dr Patel £	Dr Green £	Dr Jones £	Total £
Provision brought forward, 1 July 1998 net of overlap relief	8600	7050	9805	3796	29 251
Payments during year					
1997/98	5100	3700	5200	2046	16 046
1998/99	3000	2750	3200	1500	10 450
1996/97 adjustments	(350)	350	1905	(300)	1605
	7750	6800	10 305	3246	28 101
Charge for:					
1996/97 adjustments	(350)	350	1905	(300)	1605
1999/2000	10 500	9450	10 945	9450	40 345
Charge for year	10 150	9800	12 850	9150	41 950
Provision carried forward 30 June 1999	11 000	10 050	12 350	9700	43 100
1998/99	3000	2750	3200	1500	10 450
1999/2000	10 500	9450	10 945	9450	40 345
Overlap relief	(2500)	(2150)	(1795)	(1250)	(7695)
	11 000	10 050	12 350	9700	43 100

Figure 11.6 Movements on partners' tax provision accounts

and its related expenditure must be shown as separate items in the income and expenditure account if it is used to pay for revenue expense items. This ensures that the expenditure is included gross for Review Body purposes.

Reimbursement of capital expenditure, both out of the management allowance and from the savings account, should be shown in the same way as grants in the fixed asset note to the accounts, thus reducing the cost of the assets to the amount contributed by the practice. In most cases this will be nil. However, capital allowances may be claimed on any net amount contributed to the cost of the asset by the practice.

The fundholding bank account

Funds held in this account are not owned by a practice's partners. Therefore the account should be clearly annotated by the bank as a fundholding account, and should not be referred to in the practice balance sheet. Any interest charged on this account should be paid from the management allowance. The partners are not entitled to any interest received on the fundholding account; it must be paid to the health authority. Therefore, such interest should not be shown as income in the partnership accounts or in partners' personal tax returns.

Practice staff reimbursement

Reimbursement out of the fundholding staff fund to the partnership must be included in the practice accounts as practice staff refunds, and care should be taken to ensure that all monies due at the year end are included. If too much or too little cash has been transferred from the fundholding bank account, a balance will appear on the fundholding balance sheet as either a debtor or creditor under the heading of general practice account, and an equal and opposite entry should appear in the partnership balance sheet.

Figure 11.7 shows the note which should appear in the partnership accounts summarising the expenditure from the fundholding management allowance and the allowance received. It will be seen that the allowance received in respect of revenue items totalled £24 500, and the relevant expenditure is shown in the income and expenditure account in Figure 11.1. The allowance received to reimburse capital acquisitions totalled nil in 1999 and £6000 in 1998, which was set off against the cost of those items in the fixed assets note, thereby reducing the value of the fixed assets on the balance sheet.

Fundholding management allowance

	1999 £		1998 £
Allowance received for capital assets	–		6000
Allowance received for revenue expenditure	24 500		32 600
	24 500		38 600
Capital expenditure	–		6000
Computer equipment			
Medical equipment			
Furniture and fittings			
Revenue expenditure			
Staff salaries	16 450	22 615	
Locum payments	4100	6150	
Staff training	1058	1275	
Computer costs and maintenance	1340	1082	
Accountancy fees	–	275	
Sundry expenses	1552	1203	
	24 500		32 600
Net income	24 500		38 600

Figure 11.7 Summary of expenditure from the fundholding management allowance

Partners' personal expenses

Partners' personal expenses, such as the cost of running cars, have to be included in the Partnership Tax Return whether or not they have been paid via the practice bank account and included in the partnership accounts, or have been paid personally.

Under the Self Assessment tax regime the Inland Revenue treats the assessable profits for GPs as being the profit as shown in the accounts less the total of the partners' personal expense claims and capital allowances for the same period, which must be included in the Partnership Tax Return.

Similarly, the Review Body includes partners' personal expense claims in their calculation of total expenses, and again there is no difference between claiming the expenses through the practice accounts or a personal bank account.

The treatment chosen should be that which is most equitable between the partners. If expenses are incurred by all partners at a similar level, they may be included in the partnership accounts without the risk of one partner bearing another's expenses.

However, if there is any element of personal choice which could affect expenses levels, it is much fairer to regard personal expenditure as being paid out of that partner's profit share and tax relief should be claimed on personal expenses claims. Cars are probably the best example of this kind of expenditure; partners usually prefer to buy cars costing significantly different amounts and have widely differing levels of private usage.

The proportion of allowable motoring costs is based on the business usage proportion; thus if a partner is able to claim 50% of usage as business usage, this proportion of motoring costs will be eligible for tax relief. Capital allowances are available on the car irrespective of whether it is owned by the partnership or the partner, and the same rules apply.

Examples of business expenses frequently claimed as personal expenses include:

- surgery facilities in private homes
- home study facilities
- medical books and journals
- courses and conferences
- home telephone bills
- laundry and cleaning
- spouse's salary for telephone answering, secretarial and counselling services.

Statistical analysis and review

Accountants with a lengthy and detailed knowledge of medical accounts should be able to 'read' the accounts and identify both areas for concern and areas where the practice has performed well.

Most medical accounting specialists should be able to provide a detailed statistical analysis of the accounts and interpret the results. There are many published statistics relating to GPs and some accountants have additional facilities to provide comparisons with regional data. Perhaps the most important statistics are those which provide an analysis of NHS income and benchmarking of expenditure. Statistics for gross NHS income, net NHS income, item-of-service fees and the allocation of NHS fees should be considered as a minimum. These provide good overall indicators of the practice's performance for the year when compared to national, regional and prior year's figures.

A review of the accounts is also helpful in enabling the partners to interpret the accounts and highlight good and bad areas of the practice finances. The review should cover: incoming and outgoing partners, profit-sharing arrangements, an interpretation of profit variances from previous years, a review of income and expenditure, partners' capital, and any other matters of relevance to the current or succeeding accounting period.

Partnership deed

It is important that the current, valid and signed partnership agreement be provided to the accountant with the practice's accounting records. This enables the accountant to ensure that current practice policies are reflected in the accounts.

Where a partnership agreement does not exist, the accountant may ask for a letter of representation to be signed by the partners. This is a letter which sets out many basic common practices regarding profit-sharing arrangements, etc. The letter of representation should not be used and is not intended for use as a permanent replacement for a partnership deed.

12 Taxation

For most young doctors entering general practice, the strange and arcane world of GP finance can be something of a culture shock to those more familiar with the relatively simple methods of tax and national insurance deduction at source. Having come to terms with the payment of tax under Schedule D, the various classes of national insurance and the like represent a major change and fortunate is the young GP with an advisor who is prepared to explain this to him or her, to help him or her through the period of change and to ensure that nothing works to his or her financial disadvantage.

This chapter looks at the manner in which GPs' profits are taxed under the regulations applying to all self-employed taxpayers, whether in partnership or sole practice. This chapter does not aim to set out full details of the UK tax system as it applies to GPs and readers requiring further clarification should seek expert advice or refer to further available publications.

Taxation of some kind has always been with us and presumably will remain so. It comes in several forms: taxes on income, on capital, on the estates of deceased persons, value added tax levied on goods and services, to name but a few. The average GP is likely to come across most, if not all, of these forms of taxation during his or her working life.

The regulation of all our taxes is based on Acts of Parliament passed from time to time which lay down, in general terms, the means by which those taxes will be levied and how they will be administered and collected. Each March the Chancellor of the Exchequer presents to Parliament a Budget Statement, which ultimately finds its way on to the statute book as the latest Finance Act for that year.

The Inland Revenue offices: inspection and collection

Broadly speaking, the revenue service is divided into two sections so far as the GP is concerned: the Inspector and Collector. It is the Inspector of Taxes office to whom an accountant or taxpayer submits his or her Self Assessment Tax Return. The office will be staffed by revenue officials of various grades, who will each have their separate function to perform. It is that office which will issue assessment notices, to which appeals will be sent and correspondence conducted.

The Collector of Taxes offices throughout the country, on the other hand, are responsible purely for the demand and collection of tax. It is they to whom a tax bill will be paid, who will deal with the issue of receipts and take enforcement proceedings if the tax is not paid. At times, the liaison between the two offices may not be as efficient as it should be!

The schedules

Income tax is divided into a number of schedules, each of which governs the rules for assessment of tax on incomes of various types. For most GPs, Schedules D and E are of relevance and we shall look at these in some detail.

Employment and self-employment: Schedules D and E

For most GPs it will be the tax on their incomes which will concern them the most and in which only Schedules D and E will be concerned.

Most GPs at some time will have been assessed for tax under Schedule E and have had deductions made from their salaries under PAYE. They will have, at various times, been employees of a hospital authority, GP registrars or in other forms of employment. The GP principal, on the other hand, as a self-employed practitioner is assessed under Schedule D, which in itself derives entirely from his or her status as an independent contractor.

As the method of assessment in each case is entirely different, it is important to understand how these schedules work. The main differences lie in the manner in which expenses are allowed, the basis of assessment and the dates of payment of tax. These rules apply to all self-employed taxpayers, not merely GPs. To make matters perhaps even more confusing, in many cases these two schedules overlap, with doctors receiving income simultaneously under both headings. Where this occurs in partnerships, extremely complex situations can arise. In many cases too, it is not immediately apparent whether the income from any particular appointment is to be assessed under Schedule D or Schedule E. In recent years, the Inland Revenue has looked at a number of professions, quite outside the medical world, and these have been redesignated from Schedule D to Schedule E. The benefits to the Revenue are obvious.

In the medical field, such confusion can frequently arise in the treatment of fees paid to locums or assistant doctors. Where fees are paid from practice funds to such a doctor, extreme care must be taken to ensure that the proper taxation formalities are observed. If, for instance, a practice engages a doctor at a salary of £15 000 a year and then proceeds to pay that doctor monthly, this is in every sense of the word a salary and must be taxed under PAYE. If, on the other hand, occasional locum fees are paid to different doctors, calculated on a sessional basis without any true employer/employee relationship, then it is likely that they can be treated as Schedule D income in the hands of the recipient, who will himself bear the obligation of reporting these to the Inland Revenue and paying tax on them. The Inland Revenue would normally treat a locum who is standing in for a doctor as assessable to Schedule D rather than one who is clearly an extra pair of hands and assessable under Schedule E.

Years of assessment

For everyone in the country, doctors or not, tax is organised on the basis of tax years, sometimes termed 'years of assessment' or 'fiscal years'. In all cases, and however assessed, these years run from 6 April in one calendar year to 5 April in the next. Thus, the year from 6 April 1998 to 5 April 1999 would be designated 1998/99, and that from 6 April 1999 to 5 April 2000 as 1999/2000.

The preceding year (PY) basis

Up to 1995/96, all GPs were taxed on the PY basis, which meant that for any one fiscal year the profits taxed in that year would be those generated in the accounting period ended in the previous fiscal year. Therefore, for a practice making up its accounts to, say, 30 June 1994, the profits would have been taxed in the fiscal year 1995/96.

The preceding year basis has now ended.

The transitional year

The Revenue decided that profits for the year 1996/97, known as the transitional year, were based on the average of those earned within the two accounting periods ended in 1996/97.

The current year (CY) basis of assessment

With the ending of the PY basis, a new system of taxing the self-employed was introduced, the CY basis, whereby profits are taxed on the basis of the account period ended *within* (rather than previous to) the year of assessment. Thus, profits earned in the year to 30 June 2000 will be taxed in the year 2000/2001.

By this means, those profits earned for any given year will be taxed 12 months earlier than would formerly have been the case. Figure 12.1 shows the manner in which these profits will be taxed and the years on which assessments will be raised.

ACCOUNTS YEAR ENDED 30 JUNE

Year to 30 June	Profit £	Taxed in year		Profits taxed £
1994	170 000	1995/96	(PY)	170 000
1995	180 000 ⎱	1996/97	(T)	190 000
1996	200 000 ⎰			
1997	220 000	1997/98	(CY)	220 000
1998	225 000	1998/99	(CY)	225 000
1999	245 000	1999/2000	(CY)	245 000
2000	260 000	2000/2001	(CY)	260 000

PY: Preceding year basis
CY: Current year basis
T: Transitional year

Figure 12.1 The change to current year basis

Partnerships

The vast majority of GPs practise as members of partnerships, the main characteristic of which is that they share profits in some pre-arranged ratios. Of some 33 000 GPs practising in the UK about 81% are working as members of partnerships. Almost certainly the new doctor will find this first experience of general practice as a principal, or junior partner, working his or her way to parity over an agreed period.

The tax rules for the computation of profits assessable on partnerships and individual partners are complex, and are likely to remain so. Up to 1996/97, profits have been assessed on the partnership and demands for tax issued in the partnership name. These have invariably been apportioned by the practice accountant in accordance with the personal reliefs and expenses allowed in respect of each individual partner. The actual amount of tax payable by the partnership was therefore the sum total of the individual partner's own tax liabilities. These can vary widely, even between equal members of the same partnership.

With the advent of self assessment these composite partnership assessments are no longer issued. In their place, partnership tax returns have to be submitted to the Revenue which sets out in precise terms the amount of assessable profits attributable to each individual partner. Those are then transferred to the partners' own individual tax returns and tax paid according to the rules of self assessment.

Joint and several liability

Up to 5 April 1997, partners were jointly and severally liable for the tax liability of their partnership. Thus, if one partner defaulted or could not be found when the tax fell due for settlement, the onus for payment could well fall back on his or her own (or former) partners. So far as the Inland Revenue was involved, it was no concern of theirs from whom the tax originated, so long as their demands were settled.

This was a prospect which most partnerships were only too anxious to avoid. This was, in many cases, dealt with by partnerships setting funds aside, either in a building society or bank deposit account, so that they were available when settlement was due.

This concept of joint and several liability has now ceased, except for all tax years where tax has not been settled up to and including 1996/97. Since 6 April 1997, liabilities are chargeable only to individual partners through their personal tax returns and no liability will fall on the partnership or other partners.

Income tax reserves

Those partnerships who have habitually, and as a matter of policy, set aside funds to meet these tax liabilities will have now considered carefully whether they wish to continue to do so, in the light of the ending of joint and several liability.

Experience shows that many such partnerships wish to continue to reserve funds in this manner, in order to even out their cash flow and to ensure that separate partners are not required to draw substantial cheques at six-monthly intervals. This is a policy matter which, with sound professional advice, should be considered by each individual partnership.

Self assessment

Although the Inland Revenue introduced self assessment as a simplification of the UK tax system, for many taxpeyers it was far from simple and much more confusing. It led to up to one million taxpayers being charged penalties for submitting their tax returns late, after 31 January, incurring interest and not paying the correct amount of tax payable.

Issue and submission of returns

Self assessment returns are issued to those who have generally completed tax returns previously – to all self-employed people, partners, those liable to higher rate tax, with unearned and investment income, etc. Returns are issued by the Revenue around 6 April each year.

The returns themselves, with numerous supporting schedules, require the completion of boxes and calculation of tax payable. Where it is intended that the Revenue will calculate the tax payable, the return must be submitted to the tax office by 30 September after the fiscal year concerned. Thus, for the 1998/99 year a return for that purpose must have been submitted by 30 September 1999. Where the taxpayer proposes to calculate his or her own tax liability, then the return must be submitted to the Revenue by 31 January of the following year. Failure to submit the return by the latter of these two dates will result in an immediate penalty of £100, escalating substantially where this delay is prolonged for any length of time.

Record keeping under self assessment

There are, for the first time, guidelines set down by the Inland Revenue for the keeping of records both by personal taxpayers and those in business, such as GPs. These regulations require businesses to keep full records of their business transactions, which include details of receipts and payments, cash expenses, etc. In an extreme case where records are produced and are quite clearly inadequate, the Revenue is empowered to levy penalties up to £3000.

Dates of payment of tax

Tax payable consists of first and second interim payments on 31 January and 31 July, each respectively 50% of the previous year's total liability, with a balancing payment on the following 31 January. Thus, where a practice is to pay on 31 January 2000, this payment will consist of the first interim payment of the tax for 1999/2000, together with a balancing payment from 1998/99.

Hospital remuneration in partnerships

In many partnerships, doctors receive part of the practice remuneration in the form of 'salaries', frequently for clinical assistant posts at local hospitals. Where this applies, the income will be included in the partnership accounts, invariably because of a policy of aggregation of profits from medical sources by the partnership. A clause of this type may well be included in the partnership deed.

The system by which this income is taxed is complex. Until recently, a major difficulty was caused by local tax offices insisting on taxing this on the recipient even though it was not legally his or her own money. This system has now been alleviated and tax offices will issue authority for income of this type to be paid without the deduction of tax by means of an NT coding. Negotiations to ensure this takes place should be conducted through the practice accountant.

The property-owning partnership

Surgery premises are invariably held in partnerships and these shares of ownership will frequently differ from those in which practice profits are shared. It is necessary in such circumstances to include transactions applying to the surgery ownership within the normal Schedule D assessment, but dividing the net profit or loss accruing in the shares in which the building is owned during the year of assessment. The surgery premises should always be included in the practice balance sheet, whether or not it is owned by all the partners.

Personal practice expenses

There are few areas that cause such controversy in the world of GP finance as the extent and manner in which the doctor is to claim tax relief in respect of expenses paid privately, but which involve wholly or partly an element of practice use. It is an area that is likely to bring the GP into conflict with his or her accountant and, possibly through him or her, with the Inland Revenue.

As we shall see, the attitude of the Inland Revenue has hardened considerably in recent years and, if detected, the over-claiming of these expenses by GPs can cost the doctor dearly. What we are talking about, as likely as not, are expenses which fall under a number of headings but which are likely to be paid by the doctor personally rather than through his or her partnership. Each partner will submit, or have prepared for him or her by his or her accountant, an annual claim for personal practice expenses which are allowable against tax in exactly the same manner as partnership profits are assessed, i.e. on the current year basis. Therefore, if five doctors are in a partnership making up its annual accounts to 30 June, each of them will prepare a practice expenses claim made up to 30 June annually. Doctors are not employees and should not prepare expenses claims up to a 5 April year end unless this happens to coincide with the annual accounting date of the partnership.

These expenses, once formulated and agreed with the Inland Revenue, will be allowed for tax against that partner's share of the profits and no other. In large partnerships one can find that these expenses claims for partners vary widely, normally for perfectly good reasons; there is no reason whatever why partners will have the same personal circumstances and it is quite common for there to be large differences in the amounts each partner will claim. This will inevitably have an effect on their own share of the partnership tax liability.

Partnership and personal expenses

For the vast majority of expenditure met by the doctor or, more likely, his or her partnership, there is no argument whatever and the Inland

Revenue is highly unlikely to dispute expenditure on such routine and non-controversial expenses as printing and stationery, surgery telephone bills, staff wages, locum fees, etc.

The categories of expenditure paid personally will vary between one partnership and another. It is up to the partners themselves to determine exactly what expenditure is paid out of partnership funds and what is paid privately by the partners. Whatever they decide, however, should be mutually agreed between them and ideally should be set out clearly in the partnership deed. It is important for an incoming partner to check exactly what expenses he or she will be asked to bear personally. To preserve fairness, the same rule should apply to all partners regardless of their status in the partnership.

The basic rule

The basic rule applicable to the claiming of these expenses, for Schedule D purposes, is that they must be seen by the Inland Revenue as having been expended wholly and exclusively for the purpose of the profession. Thus, the GP who pays locum fees to another doctor for covering him or her in out-of-hours duties, will without question get those fees allowed for income tax. If he or she were an employed doctor, it is highly unlikely that he or she would get them allowed because the additional qualifying word, 'necessarily', might be impossible to justify.

Claims for personal practice expenses in respect of doctors in partnership should always be made up to the same date as the practice's accounting year end, even though a doctor may have joined midway through the year. Thus, if Dr E joined his partnership on 1 February 1999 and the partnership makes up its accounts to 30 June annually, his first claim should be for the five-month period to 30 June 1999 and to the same annual date in succeeding years.

Of far greater difficulty are those expenses which the doctor pays out partially for private use and partially for practice use. Nobody, for instance, will dispute the fact that a doctor needs to use his or her car or private telephone for practice purposes; how much exactly in fractional terms that should be is another matter and in the last analysis may be the subject of negotiations between the accountant and the Inland Revenue.

A further doctrine the Inland Revenue may seek to impose is that of 'duality of purpose'. This means that if the expenditure is incurred simultaneously both for private and practice use, the expenditure will be wholly disallowable. This is subject to a number of variations, most of which the average taxpayer may well, with some justification, consider to be 'splitting hairs'. Thus, a doctor who buys his or her suits to use in his or her consulting room would be unable to obtain any tax relief for that expenditure. The Revenue considers this to be primarily for a private purpose with some incidental element of practice use. On the other hand, the same principle is unlikely to be applied to such expenses as motor cars. The Inland Revenue fully accepts that there is an element of practice use which is quite clearly allowable. By the same token there will be an element of private use which must be disallowed.

The Inland Revenue attitude

It is fair to say that, historically, GPs have received generous treatment from the Inland Revenue in the scrutiny of their expenses claims. However, there is clear evidence of a change in approach in more recent years and following the introduction of self assessment.

As part of a general hardening of attitude to self-employed taxpayers, expenses claims in general are subject to much greater scrutiny than has always been the case in the past. For self-employed GPs, both medical and dental, there is some evidence that their accounts and claims have been subject to a particularly close watch and that Inspectors of Taxes have queried such claims under a number of headings. It seems unlikely that this process will ease with the advent of self assessment.

Experience does tend to show that salaries paid to wives/spouses, motor expenses, practice use of houses and telephone costs are particularly vulnerable. Estimated expenditure should not be included.

Where the Revenue is able to establish a pattern of over-claiming lasting for several years, it is empowered to increase assessments retrospectively, possibly over as much as six years, seeking to collect not only lost tax but interest and penalties too. It is essential that doctors understand that the risk of unrealistic claims sparking off an in-depth investigation is increasing. In particular, it should be ensured that:

- all claims submitted are clearly justified and the expenditure has actually been expended for practice purposes
- receipts are available to support all claims, and
- where restrictions for private use are in force, they can be justified; this may include mileage logs and itemised telephone bills.

Claims showing estimated expenditure should be avoided so far as is possible. Where these are unavoidable, the fact that they are estimates should be clearly shown on claims submitted to the Revenue.

GPs should understand that when a claim is prepared on their behalf by an accountant, the onus is on them not only to keep the accountant informed of genuine expenses incurred but also to check draft claims before submission to ensure that no unjustified or incorrect claims are made. A GP should be asked to sign the claim as correct before it is submitted to the Inland Revenue.

What can be claimed?

Before we go on to look at the various types of claim which might be made, these can fall in a number of generalised categories:

- expenditure paid personally by the doctor but which can quite clearly be demonstrated as being solely for practice purposes, such as medical equipment, medical journals, subscriptions, etc.
- such expenses as are partially practice and partially private use, such as home telephone, motor cars, etc.
- expenses the doctor wishes to claim but can produce no hard and fast evidence for and where estimates may be submitted. As outlined above, claims of this nature are particularly at risk of attracting unwanted Revenue attention.

Doctors frequently ask 'What claims am I entitled to make?'. The short answer is that he or she has no absolute entitlement to claim anything at all. He or she can look for ever at the Income Tax Acts and find no reference to doctors' cars, houses and the like. Indeed he or she may claim whatever he or she wishes but, as has been pointed out, claiming it and having it allowed by the Revenue are two entirely separate matters. The days of over-claiming expenditure and hoping that the Inland Revenue would allow it through 'on the nod' are gone; the penalties for over-claiming make it perfectly clear that the game is not worth the candle.

The preparation of claims of this nature can cause controversy between the GP and his or her accountant. Let it be clearly understood therefore that the accountant who advises his or her client to moderate claims to a level that will be acceptable to the Revenue, yet which at the same time does not deprive the doctor of any tax relief to which he or she might legitimately be due, is doing no more than attempting to protect his or her client in advance from the excesses of an Inland Revenue enquiry. He or she is acting with the long-term interests of the client at heart and the GP should accept and be grateful for advice of this nature.

Who should submit the claim?

In the rare case of a doctor who does not engage an accountant to act for him or her, that GP will submit and formulate the claim himself or herself, agreeing this with the Inland Revenue. Whether this is a process in the best interests of the GP is another matter; he or she has no specialist knowledge in dealing with the local Inspector of Taxes and this may well be better left to a professional accountant who is an expert at negotiations of this nature.

If the doctor is in sole practice the claim would normally be produced as part of his or her practice accounts without the necessity for submitting separate claims and no undue difficulty would arise here. It is in the case of doctors in partnerships where problems can arise as to exactly by whom the claim is to be prepared.

At times one comes across instances in partnerships where the doctors choose to have separate accountants to deal with their personal affairs. This is their own prerogative and nobody would seek to take this from them. However, it should be accepted that the accountant who deals with the partnership may well have a superior knowledge of the negotiations which have been conducted with the Inspector of Taxes and there are excellent reasons why, again, the same accountant should act for all the partners in submitting these claims. It may be that he or she is able to obtain some sort of omnibus agreement from the Inland Revenue, very much to the partners' own advantage. Only if he or she is acting for all the partners in a practice can they best be able to take advantage of this.

The submission of claims by separate accountants may be done on entirely different bases and if only one of these claims provokes an enquiry from the Inland Revenue, this could spread to all the doctors in the partnership.

All claims have to be included in the partnership tax return and this has to be signed by the nominated or representative partner from within the partnership on behalf of all of the partners.

Practice use of home

The vast majority of doctors in general practice will use their home to a greater or lesser degree for practice purposes. Some, with no other central surgery, or sole practitioners whose only surgery is in part of their house, will have a perfectly legitimate claim for a major share of the costs of running the house. At the other end of the scale one will come across the

GP, probably living several miles away from the practice area who uses his or her house mainly for occasional study or reference purposes. The claims which these two doctors can justify will in practice be extremely different. Since the setting up of out-of-hours rotas the practice use of the GP's home may have been significantly reduced.

Proportion of house expenses

Claims are frequently made for practice use of doctors' houses, based on the proportion the practice use of the house bears to the total floor area or by some similar means. Such claims, possibly when extended to include qualifying repairs expenditure and by excess mortgage interest, can at times be very substantial.

To ensure that such claims are justified and in an effort to avoid constant Revenue enquiries, it is generally considered that claims of this nature can only be justified when:

1 There is clear evidence of the use of the house for consulting or treatment of patients on a regular basis.

2 A professional plate is displayed outside the house. Though not mandatory, this could make the acceptance of a borderline claim more likely.

3 There is an appropriate entry in the local telephone directory.

4 The house is either within, or adjacent to, the practice area.

5 If the claim is to be fully justified, point 1 above must apply.

Having established that the basis for such a claim exists, it is necessary then to go on and calculate the fractional cost of the total house expenses to be claimed. The method usually employed and which is invariably acceptable to the Inland Revenue, is to award an arbitrary points figure to every room in the house, more or less dependent on its size, and then to allocate those points between practice and private use. The system will at times be adapted to a system based on floor areas, but this may be felt an over-complication and may well give rise to an identical result.

For instance, if there is a study where patients are seen and which is used for no other purpose, the whole of the points attributable to this room can be allocated to practice use. Conversely it is unlikely that an upstairs bedroom or bathroom can be allocated other than wholly for private use. The actual expenses to be included in the claim will be the normal running costs of the house, but excluding capital expenditure.

As stated above, the introduction of out-of-hours rotas may substantially reduce the justification of such claims.

Study allowance

Where the house is not regularly used for consultations but the doctor, nevertheless, spends time working at home, it is much less contentious to claim a 'study allowance', based on a lump sum estimate of the additional cost to the doctor of using his house for that purpose. A typical annual claim might be:

£1.00 per hour for 10 hours per week over 46 weeks a year = £460.

Alternatively, a round sum per week could be claimed.

Capital gains tax

One reason that frequently deters GPs from making a claim for house expenses is that they have been advised, probably incorrectly, that in the event of the house being sold at a profit at some time in the future, they will be liable for capital gains tax on a proportion of a gain realised. This is, in fact, not the case. In such circumstances CGT would not be charged unless there was some part of the house that was used exclusively for practice purposes. Even if this were the case and the doctor acquired a replacement house, also to be used in his or her practice, it is likely that the 'roll-over' relief could be claimed.

Although by no means impossible, experience does show that it is highly unlikely that a GP selling a house that has been partially used in his or her practice will give rise to an actual charge upon which CGT is payable.

The whole subject of CGT on GPs' houses is extremely complex and specialist professional advice should always be sought in such an instance. Suffice to say here that no doctor should be dissuaded from making a legitimate claim for house expenses merely by the prospect, however remote, of having to pay CGT at some time in the future.

Some other claims may include the following.

- **Medical subscriptions:** All GPs pay their registration fee to the GMC and will also subscribe to one of the medical protection societies. They may also be members of the BMA, RCGP and several other societies of a more specific nature within the profession. Care should be taken to see that all these subscriptions are properly recorded and claimed.

- **Charitable and other donations:** Some GPs will make donations to local charities and, provided these are of a reasonable amount, the local Inspector of Taxes will allow them against profits and these again should be properly recorded.

- **Medical books and journals:** Although many GPs receive most literature free of charge, there are still those who subscribe regularly to medical journals, as well as purchasing books.

- **Locum fees, etc.:** Many GPs make payments to locums for temporarily looking after their practice, as well as payments for deputising and relief services. In many cases, depending largely on clauses in the partnership deed, these may be made personally by the partners rather than out of partnership funds.

- **Security expenses:** Some doctors keep valuable drugs and equipment in their houses, and the necessity for expenditure on some form of security is obvious. The installation of burglar alarms, annual maintenance of these, provision of security locks, etc. may be justifiable for tax purposes.

- **Bank charges:** GPs often use their own private bank account to some degree for practice purposes, e.g. by paying part of their house costs, motor expenses and other sundry items from their private account. If a charge is made by the bank for use of this account, a proportion of the charges (but not interest) can be included in the claim.

- **Cleaning and laundry:** Here again, most of this expense is likely to be paid from the partnership but, if privately paid, the laundry of overalls, protective clothing etc., should be claimed. Claims for the cleaning of normal wear, such as suits and dresses, is unlikely to be accepted unless a particularly good case can be made. Claims for the purchase of such ordinary items of clothing will not be allowed under any circumstances.

- **Medical instruments:** The upkeep of cleaning and replacing medical equipment is again a perfectly proper claim and all amounts should be carefully listed and included under this heading.

- **Waiting room papers and flowers:** If the house is regularly used for seeing patients then it may be justifiable to claim such items.

- **Accountancy fees:** Most of the practice accountancy bills will be paid from partnership funds but if any charges are made to individual doctors for personal expenses claims, etc., these should be claimed. No claim can be made, however the bill is paid, for dealing with a doctor's personal income tax return.

- **Insurance premiums:** The insurance on the house will normally be included in a house expenses claim. Motor insurance should be included in the claim for car expenses. There are, however, a few premiums which can be included under general practice expenses, including public liability insurance and medical surgical equipment. Life assurance payments do not qualify for relief.

- **'Locum insurance' payments:** For many years it was accepted that where doctors paid into policies which provided a benefit in the event of sickness or accident, there was no tax relief on those premiums. This ruling has now changed, with an announcement by the Inland Revenue during 1996 that where those premiums were paid on genuine locum insurance policies, i.e. those which provide for a repayment of locum costs incurred, then the premiums on those policies will be allowable for tax purposes. In the event of a benefit being paid under the policy, any amount received would then rank as chargeable income in the hands of the recipient.

  It must be emphasised that the majority of these policies are written as permanent health insurance policies, which provide for the payment of a lump sum in the event of absence through sickness or injury, whether or not locums are engaged. These premiums will continue to be disallowed for tax purposes, although any benefit will continue to be not chargeable to tax.

- **Courses, conferences, etc.:** In many cases, costs of attending courses are refunded from NHS sources and, where no net cost is met by the GP, obviously no claim can be made. However, there are other conferences that can be attended at the GP's own cost and a claim must be made for these. Difficulty may be experienced in having claims for major overseas conferences accepted. If accompanied by a spouse, the Inspector of Taxes is likely to insist that his or her share of the costs is excluded from the claim.

- **Private telephone bills:** In some partnerships, it is the policy of the practice that all private telephone accounts are paid from partnership funds. However, in other cases, these will be met personally and a proportion of the cost of the calls should be included in the claim. This will be a matter of record and negotiation. Some Inspectors of Taxes will also allow a proportion of the rental charge. VAT is included on private telephone bills and this should also be included.

- **Photographic expenses:** Many GPs use cameras for genuine medical reasons, often in connection with training purposes. This is a perfectly reasonable claim to make, although here again some element of private use may have to be taken into account.

- **Maintenance of approach:** The cost of maintaining the garden and surroundings of the house used by the practice can be claimed in several ways. The actual cost of the upkeep of the approach to the house, to the extent that this is likely to be used by patients, is a proper claim either by inclusion in an overall claim for house expenses or separately.

However, with fewer visits by patients to a doctor's home, this expense is not now normally justifiable.

- **Computers and technical equipment:** The use by GPs of personally owned computers, video equipment, etc., is increasing. Where such equipment is bought and retained in the doctor's private house, some difficulty may be experienced in having the claim agreed as the Revenue is aware that this is likely to be used to a large degree for private and recreational purposes. If, however, such equipment were bought by the practice, included as a partnership asset and retained in the surgery, little difficulty is likely to be encountered.

National insurance

The young GP principal will find that national insurance is no longer deducted from his or her salary. These Class 1 contributions, paid by employees only, are deducted automatically and are calculated by the employer. There is no action the employed doctor need take. A self-employed GP will be liable to pay NIC under Class 2 and Class 4. Class 2 contributions are a weekly payment which are normally paid by direct debit to a bank account.

The young doctor joining a practice as a principal must be extremely careful to ensure that he or she registers as self-employed and pays these contributions as and when they fall due. Failure to do so could well result in a large bill submitted at some time in the future.

Class 4 contributions are paid with the annual tax demand in the two half-yearly payments on 31 January and 31 July.

13 Superannuation

Many GPs do not take an interest in their pensions until just before they retire. Though understandable, this may be unfortunate because at this late stage the opportunities to change pension arrangements are very limited. Ideally, everyone should be familiar with their pension arrangements and keep them under review.

The NHS pension scheme (NHSPS)

The NHSPS has two distinct benefit structures: one for independent contractors (mainly GPs) and one for salaried employees (including hospital doctors). Salaried employees are pensioned on a traditional final salary/ years of service basis. GPs on the other hand are pensioned using a unique method which takes into account all superannuable income earned through-out their careers. This method was specifically designed for GPs so as to take account of their career pattern, i.e. earnings tend to peak earlier and may even decline as they approach retirement.

Membership of the NHSPS

Membership of the scheme is open to principal practitioners, associates and assistants, but not locums. GP registrars and salaried GPs are also eligible to join but are pensioned using the salaried employee method rather than the special GP method.

Superannuable income

For pension purposes, GP income is divided into three groups, as set out in Box 13.1.

Contributions

GPs contribute 6% of their superannuable income. Although self-employed and therefore not statutorily entitled to tax relief, GPs do receive tax relief as a result of a special extra-statutory concession.

Superannuable practice income will be divided among the partners by the health authority according to their profit-sharing ratios. The health authority will provide an annual statement (form SD86C) to GPs showing the superannuable income credited to them during the year ending 31 March. This information needs to be checked carefully on receipt.

Dynamising

Because all NHS superannuable income earned throughout a career is taken into account in calculating a GP's pension, it is essential that this

Box 13.1: The NHS pension scheme – superannuable income

Group 1: Non-superannuable payments

These are treated as consisting solely of the reimbursement of expenses. The types of payments are:

- payments and notional reimbursements under the schemes for rent and rates, and for practice staff
- locum payments under the scheme for additional payments during sickness and confinement
- prolonged study leave locum payments
- locum payments for single-handed rural GPs attending training courses
- associate allowance
- payments under the doctors' retainer scheme
- net ingredient cost, container allowances and VAT paid in respect of the supply of drugs and medicines
- all payments (except the trainers' grant) made in respect of a GP registrar
- payments under the out-of-hours development scheme
- additions to basic practice allowance for the employment of an assistant
- payments made in accordance with SFA 57: LIZ Workforce Flexibilities
    - (i)   Type 3 IPA
    - (ii)   LIZ collaborative working allowance
    - (iii)   LIZ associate doctor payment
    - (iv)   LIZ assistants scheme

Group 2: Fully superannuable payments (100%)

These are treated as consisting solely of net remuneration and no deduction is made for expenses. The types of payments are:

- seniority allowance
- a training grant under the trainee practitioner scheme
- target payments
- additions to basic practice allowance for practice in a designated area

Box 13.1: *continued*

- inducement payments
- initial practice allowance (types 1 and 2 only)

Group 3: Partly superannuable payments

These are treated as consisting partly of net remuneration and partly as reimbursement of expenses. The superannuable element of these payments is a percentage which is reviewed annually (currently 65.5% with the expenses element being 34.5%). The types of payments are:

- basic practice allowance (BPA)
- standard capitation fees
- deprivation fees
- maternity medical services fees
- contraceptive services fees
- payments for temporary residents and immediately necessary treatment
- fees for emergency treatment, dental haemorrhage arrest and anaesthetic fees
- night consultation fees
- capitation addition for out-of-hours cover
- dispensing fees, on-cost, oxygen therapy service rents, and fees paid for supply of drugs and appliances
- postgraduate education allowance
- registration fees
- child health surveillance fees
- minor surgery sessional fees
- payments for health promotion programmes and chronic disease management
- rural practice payments
- fees for vaccination and immunisation carried out for reasons of public policy

income is protected against inflation over the years. This protection is provided by the procedure known as dynamising. This involves the GP's superannuable income being uprated by a factor which reflects the annual Review Body award. Dynamised income for every year of the GP's career is added together and this total figure is used to calculate the pension (see below). The uprating factors for 1999 are shown in Box 13.2.

Box 13.2: Uprating (dynamising) factors applied to GPs' superannuable pay to calculate pension

Year ending 31 March	Medical practitioner
1949	28.816
1950	28.816
1951	26.657
1952	26.657
1953	26.657
1954	26.657
1955	26.657
1956	26.657
1957	26.525
1958	24.078
1959	23.745
1960	22.701
1961	21.706
1962	21.706
1963	21.706
1964	19.039
1965	19.039
1966	17.310
1967	16.087
1968	12.983
1969	12.725
1970	12.009
1971	10.008
1972	09.264
1973	08.616
1974	08.354
1975	07.642
1976	05.499

Box 13.2: *continued*

Year ending 31 March	Medical practitioner
1977	05.359
1978	05.158
1979	03.955
1980	03.363
1981	02.833
1982	02.673
1983	02.530
1984	02.368
1985	02.222
1986	02.069
1987	01.947
1988	01.790
1989	01.668
1990	01.544
1991	01.428
1992	01.281
1993	01.201
1994	01.183
1995	01.147
1996	01.113
1997	01.080
1998	01.044
1999	01.000

Pension

A GP principal's pension is calculated by multiplying total dynamised income by 1.4%. For example, a doctor who has worked for 37 years as a GP and accumulated total dynamised income of £1 665 000:

Pension is: £1 665 000 × 1.4% = £23 310.

The pension is increased in line with the retail prices index each year.

Lump sum

In addition, there is a tax-free lump sum of three times the pension. In the above example, the lump sum would be:

$$£23\ 310 \times 3 = £69\ 930$$

However, for married men, service before 1972 attracts lump sum at only one times the pension, not three times. They will therefore have a lump sum less than three times pension unless they paid extra contributions in order to purchase the full unreduced lump sum (see below).

Other scheme benefits

These include:

- a widow's pension of 50% of the doctor's pension. For a female doctor, the widower's pension is 50% of the doctor's pension earned since 1988 only
- children's allowance if a GP dies and has children under the age of 17 or in full-time education
- tax-free lump sum death gratuity
- insurance benefits including enhanced pension on ill health retirement or if redundant from a hospital post
- separate injury benefits scheme providing a pension and lump sum if a GP is unable to work as a result of injury or illness caused by their NHS work.

Salaried service before becoming a GP principal

If this is more than 10 years it is pensioned separately using the salaried employee method mentioned above. If the pre-GP service is less than 10 years, it is pensioned as part of the GP pension if this produces a better result. The following example shows how this is done.

If a doctor worked for three years in a hospital followed by 37 years as a GP principal, the GP pension would be increased as follows:

Hospital service	3
GP service	37
Total service	40

Enhancement factor	40/37
GP pension	$£23\,310 \times 40/37 = £25\,200$
Lump sum	$£25\,200 \times 3 = £75\,600$

Salaried service after becoming a GP

If this totals less than one whole-time year, the income is added to GP superannuable income and pensioned using the GP method.

If it is more than one whole-time year, it is pensioned separately using the salaried employee method.

Purchasing extra benefits

Because GPs do not qualify and enter the NHS pension scheme until about age 24, they cannot achieve the maximum permitted service of 40 years in the scheme by age 60, unless they purchase extra benefits. An additional 9% of superannuable income can be used to buy these extra benefits, making a total contribution of 15%, all of which attracts tax relief.

The following options are available to build up a bigger pension and lump sum at retirement:

- **Buying the unreduced lump sum**: This is only necessary for married men with service before 1972, as explained above, and ensures that the lump sum will be three times the pension.

- **Added years**: Buying added years of scheme membership will result in extra benefits in the same format as in the NHS pension scheme generally, i.e. an extra index-linked pension and an extra tax-free lump sum of three times that pension. Added years also provide additional insurance cover as the added years contract will be honoured in full if the GP dies in service or retires on health grounds before age 60.

- **Additional voluntary contributions/free standing additional voluntary contributions (AVCs/FSAVCs)**: Contributions in this case are invested and will provide an extra pension (but not an extra lump sum), the size of which will depend on:
  - the amount of money invested (up to the 9% limit)
  - the success of the investment
  - annuity (interest) rates prevailing at retirement. The higher the level of interest rates, the bigger the pension (annuity) which can be purchased with the investment fund and vice versa

– the amount deducted by the AVC/FSAVC provider by way of commission and administrative charges.

AVCs are an in-house arrangement organised by the NHS scheme through the Equitable Life company. FSAVCs can be purchased through a provider of your choice. As a general rule, AVCs are likely to be better value than FSAVCs because the level of charges is lower. This is also the expressed view of the NHS pension scheme itself. With AVC/FSAVCs, it is only possible for GPs to achieve 38.1 years of service by age 60 whereas by using added years, the maximum entitlement of 40 years' service can be reached. GPs cannot forego tax relief on their NHS scheme contributions (see below) if they are contributing to an AVC/FSAVC contract but they can do so if they are purchasing added years.

The advantages and disadvantages of added years and AVCs/FSAVCs are summarised in Box 13.3. FSAVCs generate a commission for the seller,

---

Box 13.3: Added years/AVCs/FSAVCs

Scheme feature	Added years	AVCs	FSAVCs
Contributions	Cannot vary	Variable and flexible	Variable and flexible
Benefit limits	40 years at age 60	Equivalent of 38.1 years at age 60	Equivalent of 38.1 years atage 60
GPs not claiming tax relief on NHS scheme contributions	Available	Not available	Not available
Widows'/ widowers'* and children's benefits	Available at no extra cost	Available at extra cost	Available at extra cost
Death in service/ ill health benefits	Service usually enhanced	Based on size of fund	Based on size of fund
Extra lump sum	Three times extra pension	Not available	Not available
Indexing of pension	Linked to retail prices index	Available with lower pension	Available with lower pension

Box 13.3: *continued*

Scheme feature	Added years	AVCs	FSAVCs
Tax relief on contributions	Must not exceed 15% of superannuable income	Must not exceed 15% of taxable income	Must not exceed 15% of taxable income
Dependent on investment returns	No	Yes	Yes
Dependent on annuity rates at retirement	No	Yes	Yes
Charges and commissions	None	Low	Take care

*Widowers from 6 April 1988

whereas added years and AVCs do not, and care needs to be taken if a financial adviser recommends an FSAVC. The BMA Superannuation Department guidance note entitled *Improving Pension and Lump Sum Benefits* and its *FSAVC Factsheet* provide further information. These are available from BMA local offices. If still in doubt, independent financial advice can be obtained from BMA Services.

Personal pension plans (PPPs)

'Topping up' – using income not taken into account for NHS pension scheme purposes

In this case, the income available for a PPP is the difference between the net Schedule D assessment and the NHS superannuable income in any tax year.

Renouncing tax relief

Because GPs can only claim tax relief on their NHS pension scheme contributions by means of a special extra-statutory concession, they are in the unique position of being able to forego this tax relief but remain in the NHS scheme and pension their income in a PPP as well. In effect, this means that NHS superannuable income may be pensioned twice. This is an attractive option but the higher outgoings involved need to be balanced against the pension benefits eventually accruing.

Spouses' pensions

GPs may contribute towards a PPP for a spouse employed by the practice, if the spense has not joined the NHS pension scheme.

Box 13.4: Details of pensions agencies

England and Wales:
NHS Pensions Agency
Hesketh House
200–220 Broadway
Fleetwood
Lancashire
FY7 8LG
Tel: (01253) 774774

Scotland:
Scottish Office Pensions Agency
St Margaret's House
151 London Road
Edinburgh
EH8 7TG
Tel: (0131) 244 3585 or (0131) 556 8400

Northern Ireland:
Health and Personal Social Services
Superannuation Branch (HRD 6)
Waterside House
75 Duke Street
Londonderry
BT47 1FP
Tel: (01504) 319000

PPPs: taking further advice

The arrangements summarised above are complicated and GPs thinking of using them should be sure to take specialist advice from their accountants or other reputable source. Independent financial advice can be obtained from BMA Services.

14 Primary care groups and primary care trusts

Where to obtain advice and assistance

The BMA's General Practitioners Committee has published guidance and advice on the establishment of primary care groups and primary care trusts. Health authorities should be able to supply circulars and guidance published by the Health Department.

The BMA web site is at www.bma.org.uk

LMCs should be able to advise on PCG and PCT developments locally.

This chapter outlines the basic structure of primary care groups (PCGs) and primary care trusts (PCTs) and explains their role in developing a primary care-led NHS. PCGs and PCTs (the latter due to begin operating from 1 April 2000) have been introduced as result of the government's NHS reforms announced in December 1997. PCGs and PCTs are designed to maintain the influence of primary care over the commissioning of patient services that was previously undertaken by fundholding GPs and health authorities.

Under the fundholding scheme only those practices within the scheme held a budget for commissioning patient services. For the patients of non-fundholding GPs, the health authority was responsible for purchasing secondary care. With the creation of PCGs and PCTs there will be a single purchasing budget covering all the patients of all practices within the neighbourhood. The changes in purchasing responsibility brought about by the reforms are outlined in Box 14.1.

Box 14.1: The reforms to the NHS internal market

Before 1 April 1999	After 1 April 1999	After 1 April 2000
Purchasers		
health authorities fundholding practices GP commissioning groups	HA/PCGs	HA/PCGs PCTs
Providers		
NHS trust hospitals practices private providers	NHS trust hospitals practices	NHS trust hospitals practices PCTs (level 4)

What are primary care groups and primary care trusts?

PCGs and PCTs are the new bodies responsible for ensuring the delivery of and improving the quality of services to patients. From 1 April 1999 every general practice in England has been part of a PCG which will lead the development of primary care and commission secondary care services for the local population. In Wales, local health groups perform very similar functions.

All PCGs operate as a subcommittee of the health authority. The functions they carry out are delegated to them by the health authority in accordance with guidance from the NHS Executive. From 1 April 2000 PCGs will, subject to the Secretary of State's approval, be able to convert themselves into primary care trusts becoming free-standing NHS bodies independent of direct health authority control.

In 1999–2000 there were 481 PCGs established in England each comprising around 50 GPs and serving an average patient population of around 100 000. The boundaries of PCGs were determined in consultation with local GPs, patient organisations and local authorities, and were intended to reflect natural communities of patients. Every practice and patient is a member of a single PCG.

Each PCG has the task of advising the health authority on commissioning secondary care services for the local population and for deciding local priorities for developing primary care services and practices. In particular, PCGs determine the level of support that practices can obtain for extra staff or for new or improved premises or computers. In addition PCGs are expected to play a leading role in improving the quality of patient services and in developing and supporting clinical governance amongst health professionals.

PCTs have similar responsibilities but are free-standing bodies independent of the health authority and, in some cases, additionally responsible for providing community patient services. They have greater independence than PCGs and are able to employ their own staff.

The four types of PCG are shown in Box 14.2.

Box 14.2: Primary care groups and primary care trusts

Level 1	A PCG which advises the health authority on its commissioning of patient services
Level 2	A PCG which takes devolved responsibility for managing the budget for healthcare for the PCG's population as part of the health authority
Level 3	A PCT which is a free-standing statutory body accountable to the health authority for commissioning patient services but no longer part of the health authority
Level 4	A PCT which is a free-standing statutory body accountable to the health authority for commissioning patient services, with the additional responsibility of providing community health services for the population

---

What are PCGs' and PCTs' responsibilities?

Broadly the main responsibilities of PCGs and PCTs are:

- to improve the health of the community by addressing the health needs of the local population, promoting the health of the population, and working with other organisations to deliver effective and appropriate care

- to develop primary and community health services through clinical governance (see below), professional development, education and training, and by investing in improving primary care services
- to commission secondary care services
- to determine levels of reimbursement for GPs' staff, premises and computers under the Red Book (Statement of Fees and Allowances)
- to manage within the financial resources available to them for patient care (a unified budget for prescribing, hospital and community health services, and expenditure on GP practices)
- to devise incentive arrangements for effective performance which improve health outcomes for patients

and, in the case of Level 4 PCTs:

- to provide a range of community health services.

How do PCGs carry out their functions?

All PCGs have a board which is a subcommittee of the local health authority. It is the PCG board that controls and is accountable for the activities of the PCG. The board is expected to involve local GPs, other health professionals and patients in its decision making through open meetings with regular feedback.

Boards are required to adopt a corporate approach to making their decisions. They must base their deliberations on the needs of all the patients for whom the PCG is responsible. All board members (including GP representatives) are responsible for looking after the interests of the PCG population as a whole – not just the patients of their own practice.

Each board meets regularly and has its own staff (within the health authority) to carry out its decisions. PCGs are accountable to the health authority and are expected to keep health professionals and the public informed of their activities and decisions. Nationally, £135 million was made available to health authorities in 1999–2000 to support PCG management costs. Each PCG is expected to negotiate an appropriate level of financial support from its host health authority.

Who is on the PCG board?

The PCG board is made up of GPs, nurses, lay and social services representatives together with a chief executive. The government has repeatedly stated that it wishes to see local health professionals play a greater role in the management and development of patient services.

To ensure the influence of primary care professionals GPs are, if they wish, able to insist that a majority of board members are GPs appointed by local practices. They are also able to insist upon there being a GP chairman appointed by the board. The board structure is outlined in Box 14.3.

Box 14.3: PCG board structure

Depending on local GP choice the board structure of each PCG is:

4–7 GPs

2 nurses

1 PCG chief executive

1 social services representative

1 lay person appointed by the health authority

1 health authority non-executive director

Guidance issued by the NHS Executive has made clear that GP appointments to the boards of PCGs should carry the confidence of colleagues. In the majority of cases, local elections took place to select the GP board members. To ensure proper representation of all GPs some PCGs have reserved places for particular categories of GP, for example single-handed practitioners, on the board.

Nurse representatives can similarly be appointed following local elections or may be selected by the health authority. The health authority is also responsible for choosing the lay representative and for securing the nomination of a social services representative from the local authority.

PCG board members are eligible for the allowances outlined in Box 14.4 to reimburse them for their time and, in the case of GPs, any locum support to cover absence from practices.

How do PCTs differ from PCGs?

PCTs have all the responsibilities of PCGs but are independent of the health authority and, in the case of Level 4 PCTs, have the additional function of

---

Box 14.4: PCG board members' remuneration and allowances

PCG chairmen

	PCG population <75 000	PCG population >75 000
Level 1 – advisory PCG	Up to £11 445	Up to £13 225
Level 2 – PCG with delegated budget	Up to £13 225	Up to £15 125

PCG board members

Level 1 – advisory PCG	Up to £2700 per annum (payable as a monthly allowance or as sessional payments to a ceiling of £2700)
Level 2 – PCG with delegated budget	Up to £4000 per annum (payable as a monthly allowance or as sessional payments up to a ceiling of £4000)

Compensatory allowances to pay for GP locum cover are:

PCG board member	Up to £3000 per annum
PCG chairman (GP with full-time practice commitment)	Up to £6000 per annum
PCG chairman (GP with a less than full-time practice commitment)	Up to £3000 per annum

No provision has been made for the annual uprating of these allowances.

---

providing community health services. Because they are independent of the health authority they have a different board structure and governance arrangements designed to achieve a balance between the influence of health professionals and public accountability.

PCTs operate under the overall supervision of a lay majority board, which is appointed directly by the Secretary of State. There is no provision for a GP majority on the board or for the appointment of a GP chairman. In order to maintain the influence of health professionals each PCT has an executive where primary care and community care professionals are in the majority. The typical composition of a PCT board is set out in Box 14.5.

Box 14.5: PCT board structure

chairman (appointed by the Secretary of State)

5 lay members (appointed by the Secretary of State)

chief executive

finance director

3 professional members drawn from the PCT executive (typically one clinical governance director, one GP and one nurse)

The professional executive has been described as the 'engine room' of the PCT. It brings together representatives of all the health professionals within the PCT and is expected to initiate detailed thinking on priorities, service policies and investment plans. For Level 3 PCTs the membership of the executive is expected to reflect the professional membership of a PCG (up to seven GPs, two nurses, a public health professional and a social services representative). For Level 4 PCTs the membership of the executive does not guarantee a GP majority.

PCTs can only be established at the direction of the Secretary of State following the submission of detailed proposals and after a process of local consultation has been undertaken by the health authority.

The criteria that govern the establishment of a PCT are that:

- there is broad local support for the proposal among GPs
- a clear vision has been set out establishing the health benefits that the PCT will bring backed by agreed standards and targets
- the PCT will make an effective contribution to local health improvement plans (in accordance with the health authority's Health Improvement Programme)
- there are effective arrangements for developing clinical standards, including at practice level
- there are adequate monitoring arrangements
- there has been an assessment of the local impact of any service change and reconfiguration
- the PCT has access to good quality human resources support
- the proposals take full account of the services to be provided by the PCT and access to those that will not be provided by the PCT.

For all PCTs approved there will be a preparatory period between establishment and the operational date. During this time board and executive members will be appointed and the PCT will advertise and recruit staff, where necessary, and enter into NHS agreements and other contracts.

What is the role of the health authority?

Health authorities are expected to facilitate the development of PCGs and PCTs and to monitor their performance. When a proposal is put forward for the creation of a PCT the health authority is responsible for undertaking the local consultation and for communicating the proposal and any responses to the Secretary of State.

All health authorities publish an annual Health Improvement Programme (HImP), developed in consultation with PCGs, PCTs, social services and other organisations, which sets out the priorities for improving the health of the local population. The HImP sets out the broad objectives of the health authority and informs the investment and purchasing decisions of local PCGs, PCTs and other agencies. The HImP includes targets for achievement against which the performance of the health authority can be judged.

Based on the HImP, every health authority has a separate accountability agreement with each of its PCGs and PCTs. These agreements set out the responsibilities of the PCG and PCT against which the health authority will monitor their performance.

Health authorities are also responsible for the local distribution of resources between PCGs and PCTs in accordance with national resource allocation formulae.

The role of the health authority under the NHS (GMS) Regulations and terms of service for GP principals remains unchanged following the establishment of PCGs and PCTs, except that PCGs (as subcommittees of the health authority) and PCTs (as independent statutory bodies) are now responsible for determining the discretionary levels of reimbursement available to GPs for their staff, premises and computers in accordance with the Red Book. PCGs and PCTs are not able to provide general medical services in their own right.

Commissioning services – long-term service agreements

With the creation of PCGs and PCTs the government has reformed the NHS internal market by eliminating the annual contracts for patient services that NHS trusts had previously been required to negotiate with fundholding GPs and with health authorities. These have been replaced with NHS service agreements. The intention is that long-term service agreements of around three years' duration and new arrangements for the more effective commissioning of specialist services will reduce bureaucracy and the amount of time spent by NHS staff in negotiating annual contracts. The intention is to encourage a more flexible system of contracting that allows both commissioners and providers to better plan service developments over a longer period.

The unified budget and practice incentives

All PCGs and PCTs receive a unified budget to meet the costs of their investments in GP staff, premises and computers, their expenditure on prescribing, and on hospital and community health services. The unified budget can be spent on all of these items in varying proportions provided that, overall, a minimum level of expenditure on GPs' staff, premises and computers is maintained. This important safeguard was negotiated by the GPC with the introduction of unified budgets to ensure that the necessary level of financial support for GP practices is maintained.

Every PCG and PCT is allocated an amount according to national resource allocation formulae designed to ensure that each PCG and PCT receives a fair share of the NHS resources available. Over time it is intended that PCGs and PCTs will move closer to the target allocations set for them according to resource allocation formulae.

To encourage the delivery of good clinical and cost-effective services PCGs and PCTs are able to operate incentive arrangements with practices. From 1 April 1999 every practice has had a devolved budget for prescribing and, should they spend less than the amount they have been allocated, are able to put a proportion of any such 'surplus' towards developing patient services.

PCGs and PCTs at Level 2 and above are able to extend the range of incentives to cover secondary care activity as well. Practices which are able to reduce costs as a result of improved clinical and more cost-effective performance are able to retain a proportion of any 'surplus' arising in accordance with any incentive scheme developed by the PCG or PCT.

The uses to which 'surpluses' from local incentive schemes can and cannot be put are strictly controlled and are summarised in Box 14.6.

Box 14.6

Practice incentive 'surplus' payments may be used for:

- the purchase of material or equipment which is to be used for the treatment of patients of the members of the practice, including diagnostic equipment, ECG machines, blood testing equipment, sterilisers, nebulisers, fetal heart detectors, cryothermic probes, defibrillators and related consumables

- payments to dieticians or counsellors providing advice on diet, lifestyle, alcohol consumption or smoking

- the purchase of material or equipment which will enhance the comfort or convenience of patients of members of the practice, including furniture, furnishings, security features, heating/air conditioning or vending machines for the practice

- the purchase of computers, including hardware and software

- non-recurring staff costs

- initiatives to improve prescribing

- the purchase of material or equipment relating to health education, including television, videos, leaflets and posters, and payment for advice on how best to disseminate health education advice to patients

- investment in existing practice premises where the improvements or development proposals are consistent with existing PCG/PCT plans

Practice incentive 'surplus' payments may not be used for:

- the purchase of services or equipment which are unconnected with healthcare

- reducing the practice's contribution to the employment costs of existing practice staff

- the purchase of land or premises

- paying off existing loans or mortgages taken out by the members of the practice or third-party landlords

- the purchase of drugs, medicines or appliances

- the purchase of hospital services

- practice premises investment where the development proposals are not consistent with PCG/PCT plans

What is clinical governance?

Every NHS organisation is now required to adhere to the concept of 'clinical governance' to ensure that the quality of patient services is constantly monitored and developed. All health authorities and NHS trusts (including PCTs) have a new statutory duty of ensuring quality.

The NHS Executive defines clinical governance as:

> *A framework through which NHS organisations are accountable for continuously improving the quality of their services and safeguarding high standards of care by creating an environment in which excellence in clinical care will flourish.*

The main components of clinical governance are identified as:

- clear lines of responsibility and accountability for the overall quality of clinical care
- a comprehensive programme of quality improvement systems (including full participation in national clinical audit, supporting and applying evidence-based practice, implementing clinical standards and guidelines, staff planning and development)
- education and training
- clear policies on managing risk
- procedures for identifying and remedying poor performance.

All PCGs and PCTs are expected to appoint a clinical governance lead with responsibility for overseeing local activity for improving and assessing clinical quality and ensuring a coordinated approach between organisations, including GP practices.

PCGs and PCTs will be supported in this role through the guidelines and audit procedures produced by the National Institute for Clinical Excellence (NICE), which has been created by the government to advise health professionals on best clinical practice. They will also receive support and advice from the NHS Executive and Commission for Health Improvement (CHI).

CHI is responsible for reviewing NHS performance and conducts a rolling programme of visits to NHS bodies. The Commission's functions are:

- providing national leadership in developing clinical governance
- scrutinising local arrangements for clinical governance
- reviewing the implementation of national guidelines published by NICE

- helping identify serious or persistent problems with standards of clinical care
- overseeing and assisting in external incident inquiries.

All health professionals, guided by their professional bodies, are expected to adhere to the concept of clinical governance.

Summary

This is only a broad overview of the role and functions of PCGs and PCTs, which are expected to develop substantially over time. The scope for PCTs to adopt new methods of delivering patients services is considerable and it is likely that some will seek to exploit opportunities under the Primary Care Act 1997 to employ GPs to provide personal medical services to patients or to engage them as independent contractors on locally negotiated terms.

At the time of writing, the government has provided a written assurance that, although these possibilities exist, no GP principal will be forced to become a salaried GP or to relinquish their independent contractor status. The choice to work under any new arrangements will be personal and voluntary according to the government.

15 Medical politics: how GPs are represented

Like their counterparts in other branches of the medical profession, GPs belong to a wide variety of representational, professional and learned bodies, and pressure groups. Some cater for the entire profession, such as the General Medical Council, BMA, the medical defence organisations and the Royal Society of Medicine; whereas others serve the interests of a minority, for example the Overseas Doctors Association and the Dispensing Doctors Association. This chapter explains how the interests of all GPs are collectively represented through their own democratic machinery, which is based on the links between LMCs and the BMA's General Practitioners Committee (GPC). There are five GPCs in all; a UK GPC, and GPCs for England, Northern Ireland, Scotland and Wales.

Because it is such a well-established profession, medicine enjoys a large measure of self-government in its relationship to the state. This self-government has generated a variety of medico-political institutions, including those which enable doctors to be represented on bodies concerned with the running of the NHS. In particular, all NHS GPs (including non-principals) are represented by UK and national GPCs and a network of 122 LMCs.

Background

The origins of the GPC and the LMCs date back to 1913, when a publicly funded health service (albeit restricted to providing GP services to a minority of the adult population) was first introduced by Lloyd George's National Insurance Act. When this legislation was proposed it made no provision for GPs to be involved in the running of the new state health service. However, the BMA was determined that the profession should have a voice and its efforts ensured that locally elected committees of GPs (LMCs) were statutorily recognised in the Act as the democratic voice of

GPs in each locality. Thus the Act required local insurance committees (the forerunners of NHS executive councils, family practitioner committees (FPCs), family health services authorities and latterly health authorities), whose task was to run this new health insurance scheme, to consult through the LMC all GPs participating in the new health service on many administrative and professional matters.

Once LMCs were established, the BMA formed a national committee based on them to represent GPs' interests in negotiations with government. This committee, the Insurance Acts Committee, the forerunner of the GMSC and subsequently the GPC, was recognised by government as the democratic voice of GPs.

The Liberal Government agreed to these arrangements for representing GPs because the success of its health insurance scheme depended on the willing cooperation of GPs. Although the profession ostensibly supported the concept of a state medical scheme it was opposed to it being provided by salaried doctors. It believed that if GPs' independent contractor status was replaced by a salaried service this would undermine their freedom to practise without state interference and affect adversely patient care. GPs and their representatives suspected that government would attempt to influence their day-to-day care of patients.

Commitment to the independent contractor status remained a guiding principle of the GMSC, the predecessor of the GPC. Had it not been for the tenacity of its forerunner (the Insurance Acts Committee) on this crucial issue, GPs could have been unwillingly sucked into a salaried service (as were their hospital colleagues in 1948). The well-tested and proven value of the contract for service with local insurance committees led to this type of contract continuing and developing within the NHS following its inception in 1948. The local insurance committees recognised that this contract worked well and sought successfully to preserve it in the new NHS structure.

Health authorities recognise LMCs

LMCs must be formally recognised by health authorities in order to carry out their statutory functions and raise funds through the statutory levy for their day-to-day operation. This statutory recognition of the LMC has parallels elsewhere in the public sector; legislation enacted in the 1940s to nationalise public utilities and major industries explicitly recognised trade unions and professional associations for negotiating and consultative purposes. The statutory recognition accorded to LMCs was granted almost 40 years earlier; the earliest example in the UK of an organisation being recognised by statute to represent those providing a publicly funded service.

Three types of functions and duties of LMCs derive from their recognition by health authorities:

- those based on the 'partnership principle' (originating in 1911): on many key issues LMCs and health authorities determine jointly what policies and actions should be implemented. This local recognition and representation ensures the efficient provision of general medical services, enabling health authorities to draw upon the goodwill and experience of local GPs. The process of consultation also ensures that the terms of service (negotiated centrally by the GPCs and Health Departments) are fairly and reasonably applied locally

- those concerned with administering the GP contract. Health authorities are obliged to consult LMCs on many issues; this is evident in the regulations governing NHS general medical services, GPs' terms of service, and the Statement of Fees and Allowances. The LMC also plays an important role in both the complaints procedure and the investigation of certain matters relating to professional conduct

- . those concerned with representing GPs as a whole.

LMCs also provide many other services for their GP constituents which vary according to local 'custom and practice'. These include handling local ethical problems, representing GPs in relations with bodies and organisations outside the NHS, and promoting the standing of general practice both in the media and among the public generally. To this end many LMCs have established close ties with MPs, local councillors, community health councils, and other professions such as nursing, health visiting and social work.

Other health service bodies

The LMC also serves as a point of reference for other NHS bodies seeking GPs' views; a perusal of LMC activities shows that this is a large part of their work. Although GPs are no longer represented, as of right, on health authorities, a few continue to serve on these bodies. In some areas, LMCs appoint doctors to serve on regional medical advisory committees, regional GP advisory subcommittees, purchasing advisory bodies, district medical advisory committees (where these are established), and also on variously named district medical liaison/executive committees, the regional GP subcommittees for postgraduate medical education, and many other ad hoc committees and working groups (clinical and administrative) at regional, district and local levels. LMCs are consulted when GPs are appointed to many offices and posts, and they play an active part in advising their local health authorities on a range of policy matters, including recently, and most importantly, the commissioning of secondary care. In short, LMCs have a continuing dialogue with other parts of the NHS. They also become involved in many other issues affecting GPs locally: examples include clinical assistants and hospital practitioner grade posts, GP hospitals and units, GP beds and access to diagnostic facilities.

LMCs' medico-political functions

The LMC is an independent, self-financing body with statutory functions (as distinct from a state-funded statutory body). Its independent status allows it to exercise medico-political and statutory functions. This duality of roles is unique and contributes to its strength. The statutory functions are mostly concerned with protecting the interests of individual GPs in relation to their contract, and also with the continuing consultations and negotiations between LMCs and health authorities. On the other hand, the medico-political functions are concerned primarily with the collective interests of GPs as a group, and they operate through a quite separate channel consisting of the annual conference of LMC representatives and the GPC.

In some areas, regional committees of LMCs provide a forum for discussing supra-district problems and exchanging ideas and experience. In these circumstances regional local medical committees provide an important link with NHSE regional offices.

Five GPCs

The five GPCs are BMA committees with authority to deal with all matters affecting NHS GPs in their various countries: UK, England, Northern Ireland, Scotland and Wales. They represent all GPs in their respective constituencies, whether or not they are members of the BMA (in fact over 70% are members).

The committees are recognised as the sole negotiating body for general practice by their relevant Health Departments and are represented in negotiation with ministers and civil servants by GPs who draw on their day-to-day experience of general practice and are assisted by full-time expert advisers. The teams are supplemented by other GPC members and legal, accountancy and other specialist advice as and when necessary.

The GPC (UK) has 83 members, a majority of whom are directly elected representatives of GPs. It meets monthly and much of its work is done by subcommittees and task groups. It is represented on most national bodies concerned with health, providing an essential medical input which is firmly rooted in the day-to-day experience of general practice. The English, Northern Ireland, Welsh and Scottish GPCs have autonomy on NHS matters exclusive to their countries.

The UK GPC's policy-making procedures operate on an annual cycle. It sends all GPs an annual report of its work in March. Individual GPs can influence policy through their LMCs, which consider the report and submit motions to the annual conference of LMC representatives held in June. This conference, comprising more than 300 GPs appointed by LMCs, is the profession's principal policy-making body. Those motions which are approved by the conference are referred to the UK GPC to implement. This democratic process gives credibility to the GPC's day-to-day activities as the representative voice of all NHS GPs.

This description of the LMC conference/GPC structure shows how GPs have exercised 'self-government' through their LMCs. Every part of the UK has at least one spokesperson on the UK GPC, a doctor working in practice who can represent its problems and express its views on issues affecting negotiations for GPs as a whole.

Negotiations with government

There is a regular cycle of meetings between the UK GPC negotiating team and a team of Health Department officials, and these are supplemented by many other meetings to deal with specific matters. Indeed, contact between the GPC secretariat and the Health Department is normally as frequent as several times each working day; thus there is a continuing dialogue between the two sides. Over the years, negotiations have covered a wide range of issues. In practice, the satisfactory completion of negotiations only occasionally results in major amendments to the Red Book and, even more rarely, amendments to the legal framework of general practice, the NHS regulations (which include the GP's terms of service). It is important to note that the Red Book, although technically part of the NHS regulations, can be amended without parliamentary approval, whereas because the NHS regulations themselves are parliamentary enactments they require parliamentary approval to amend their provisions.

General medical services defence fund

This representative system involves a considerable expenditure of time and money, and the defence fund (first established in 1913) is the main source of funds for running it. The term 'defence' may appear to be a misnomer if narrowly defined to apply only to some form of direct action against government (e.g. the collection of undated resignations from the NHS); however, the GPCs' work, together with that of their subcommittees and working groups, is aimed at defending GPs' interests both collectively and individually, even though the profession may not be engaged in a confrontation with government on any specific issue. All this activity costs money; it could be described as the price the profession has to pay for 'self-government'.

Statutory and voluntary levies

Most of the income for the defence fund comes from voluntary contributions raised by LMCs from their constituent GPs. This voluntary levy is quite distinct from the statutory levy; the latter may be used only 'for defraying the administrative expenses of the LMC, including travelling and subsistence allowances payable to its members'. Although the legislation allows LMCs (in England and Wales only) to make a compulsory statutory levy on every GP to meet these specific expenses, not all LMCs choose to do so. Each LMC determines for itself whether to raise its funds from either the voluntary levy or both the voluntary and statutory levies.

16 Eligibility to work in general practice and the GP vocational training scheme

Where to obtain advice and assistance

Advice about training for general practice is provided by regional advisers in general practice (deans or directors of postgraduate GP education) and by the joint committee on postgraduate training for general practice and RCGP. (Both the JCPTGP and RCGP can be contacted at 14 Princes Gate, London SW7 1PU, or at www.rcgp.org.uk/jcpt)

BMA members should contact their local BMA office for expert advice and assistance, particularly in relation to any problems concerning removal expenses. The GPC has a model contract of employment for GP registrars which can be obtained from local BMA offices.

The BMA web site is at www.bma.org.uk

Before 1981, when vocational training for general practice became a mandatory requirement, any fully registered medical practitioner could apply to become a GP principal as a partner or as a single-handed practitioner. Any registered doctor was also able to work as an assistant, associate, locum or retainee. However, doctors without previous GP experience were rarely admitted to the medical list because long before vocational training was made obligatory for principals, most doctors wishing to become GPs were already extending their one-year pre-registration hospital training by gaining further hospital experience, as well as filling traineeships, or sometimes assistantships, before joining a practice.

Since 1995 a doctor wishing to work in general practice in any capacity (other than doctors in training) must have completed an approved course of vocational training or have experience that is recognised as being equivalent or have a legal exemption. These requirements are set out in the NHS (vocational training for general medical practice) regulations. The body responsible for certifying eligibility to work in general practice under the regulations, and for setting the standards for general practice training throughout the UK, is the joint committee for postgraduate education in general practice (JCPTGP).

The vocational training regulations

These regulations govern entry to general practice; all doctors wanting to work in general practice as GP principals, assistants, associates, locums or retainees have to show that they have acquired a specified range of postgraduate experience. The regulations do not apply to doctors who work as whole-time practitioners in private general practice.

All doctors wishing to work in NHS general practice must have from the JCPTGP either:

- a certificate of prescribed experience issued on completion of vocational training, or
- a certificate of equivalent experience.

Certain categories of doctor have, however, a legal exemption from the requirement to hold a JCPTGP certificate or have an 'acquired right' to practise in the UK without one. Those with an exemption are doctors who:

- were already GP principals on 15 February 1981 when the regulations first applied or who were engaged in comparable duties in the armed forces at that time
- were GP principals before 15 February 1981 and who were re-admitted to the medical list before 15 February 1990
- have a recognised primary medical qualification awarded by a European Economic Area (EEA) member state other than the UK and who were established in NHS general medical practice on 31 December 1994
- provided limited general medical services (i.e. to a limited list of patients) and who were included on the medical list of a health authority as providing such services on 31 December 1994

- hold a certificate or diploma of completion of specific training for general practice (a certificate of vocational training) or a certificate of acquired rights issued in an EEA member state other than the UK.

Those with an 'acquired right' are doctors who:

- were practising as GP principals in the NHS on 31 December 1994
- are eligible to become GP principals under the NHS (vocational training) regulations by virtue of the fact that they were GP principals on or after 15 February 1981 or, if employed in the armed forces, in possession of a statement of exemption from the director general of medical services confirming employment on 15 April 1981
- worked as assistants (including on the retainer scheme) or deputies (including as a locum) in general practice on either ten separate days in the four years ending 31 December 1994 or 40 separate days in the ten years ending 31 December 1994. It should be noted that this 'acquired right' applies only to work as a deputy or assistant and does not exempt the holder from the requirement to hold a JCPTGP certificate, or exemption, to work in general practice in any other capacity
- have a recognised primary medical qualification awarded by an EEA member state other than the UK and who were established in general medical practice on 31 December 1994.

The requirement to hold a JCPTGP certificate of prescribed or equivalent experience also extends to applicants for admission to the medical list for the provision of child health surveillance, contraceptive services, maternity medical services, minor surgery services or some combination of these as a restricted services principal in the NHS. Only doctors who were included on the medical list for these services on 31 December 1994 are exempt from the requirement to hold a certificate.

Doctors with an exemption or 'acquired right' seeking to take up a post as a GP principal, associate, assistant or deputy will need to be able to prove their entitlement. For those able to demonstrate their eligibility to an 'acquired right' the JCPTGP will issue a certificate on request. For doctors who are exempt from the requirement to hold a certificate of prescribed or equivalent experience satisfactory evidence of exemption will need to be presented to prospective employers or the health authority (for example evidence of being on the medical list of a health authority before 1981).

What is prescribed experience?

The NHS (vocational training) regulations specify that to be eligible for a certificate of prescribed experience doctors must complete three years' training (or the equivalent part time) comprising:

- at least one year as a GP registrar and (for employment after 30 January 1998) to have completed all components of summative assessment

- at least one year comprising two or more hospital appointments of at least six months in each of two of the following specialties: general medicine, geriatric medicine, paediatrics, psychiatry, accident and emergency medicine and/or general surgery and obstetrics and/or gynaecology. The hospital part of training may be confined to any two of these specialties

- any remaining period may be spent on one or more of a wider range of hospital or community medicine posts or in a GP training practice. However, experience in specialties other than those listed above can contribute only a maximum of six months towards the overall training period.

The appointments must be to posts which are approved for general practice training. Regional directors of postgraduate general practice education can confirm whether or not posts are approved and can provide details of formal three-year vocational training schemes. Doctors are free to construct their own programme of training but must take care to ensure that the posts they take up are approved for training purposes.

For each separate appointment during the training period GP registrars have to obtain a 'statement of satisfactory completion' which must be presented to the JCPTGP. The 'VTR form', as it is known, will confirm the total period of employment and that the training has been completed to the supervising doctor's satisfaction. For hospital appointments the supervising doctor will be the hospital consultant and for general practice appointments the form must be signed by the GP trainer.

'Satisfactory completion' of any period of training is defined in the regulations as completing it 'in such a manner as to have acquired the medical experience which may reasonably be expected to be acquired from training of that duration in that employment'.

Legal advice confirms that satisfactory completion indicates a satisfactory level of competence has been achieved according to the assessment of the person signing the statement and this is a view that has been jointly endorsed by the GPC, JCPTGP and RCGP. Thus doctors completing any component of vocational training for general practice are expected to have achieved a satisfactory standard of competence and performance.

It is important to ensure that VTR forms are completed at the end of each training appointment as it may be more difficult to obtain them later. Where a VTR certificate is refused doctors should contact the local director of postgraduate general practice education.

Summative assessment

For any doctor starting their minimum 12 months' employment as a GP registrar after 30 January 1998 the regulations now specify that they must satisfy a test of competence which is completed at the end of their period of training called 'summative assessment'.

Summative assessment is designed to be an objective test that a GP registrar has achieved a minimum level of competence to practice independently as a GP. The competencies tested are set out in Box 16.1.

Box 16.1: The competencies to be tested by summative assessment

- factual medical knowledge which is sufficient to enable the doctor to perform the duties of a GP
- the ability to apply factual medical knowledge to the management of problems presented by patients in general practice
- effective communications both orally and in writing
- the ability to consult satisfactorily with general practice patients
- the ability to review and critically analyse the doctor's own working practices and manage any necessary change appropriately
- clinical skills
- the ability to synthesise all of the above competencies and apply them appropriately in a general practice setting

---

There are four components to summative assessment:

- a multiple choice questionnaire examination (MCQ)
- an assessment of consultation skills using video recordings
- written submission of practical work
- a report by the GP trainer.

For summative assessment to be completed successfully all four components must be passed. All GP registrars should receive an information pack including the booklet *Summative Assessment of General Practice Training*, published by the UK conference of postgraduate advisers in general practice, which gives details of the procedures and instructions for candidates.

For doctors who fail any element of summative assessment a further period of training will normally be offered. The Health Department will continue to make payments under the GP registrar scheme during this period. Doctors who are concerned that they may have trouble passing a component of summative assessment are able to make an application to the JCPTGP for their period of training to be extended if they wish. The period of additional training will not normally exceed six months (or its equivalent part time) but may, in exceptional circumstances, be extended for as long as 12 months (or its equivalent part time).

Equivalent experience

Other kinds of clinical experience which do not necessarily fulfil the criteria of prescribed experience may count as 'equivalent' to prescribed experience. For example:

- posts occupied on a less than half-time basis or for less than six months
- experience gained outside the UK
- 'electives'
- experience gained in occupational health.

If the JCPTGP is satisfied that a doctor's overall experience is indeed equivalent to that prescribed in the regulations, including summative assessment, it will issue a certificate of equivalent experience, which has the same standing as a certificate of prescribed experience and confirms the doctor's eligibility to work in general practice.

Equivalent experience provides a way of satisfying the requirements of the regulations other than by conventional vocational training. However, the experience must equate in educational terms to that prescribed in the regulations: the standardised programme of training and its variations.

The JCPTGP will require detailed evidence of any experience claimed to be equivalent and has developed a substantial body of case law which enables it to judge whether a particular range of experience satisfies the criteria. For training posts in other countries in the EEA to be accepted as equivalent experience they should be specifically approved for training in general practice by the relevant country's equivalent body to the JCPTGP. The JCPTGP is able to supply a list of such bodies on request.

Ultimately a doctor has a right of appeal to the Secretary of State against any refusal by the JCPTGP to issue a certificate of prescribed or equivalent experience.

Vocational training schemes

Normally, full vocational training for general practice involves a three-year structured scheme which is usually undertaken immediately after GMC registration. Schemes normally comprise two years in approved hospital posts as a senior house officer (SHO) and one year in a training practice as a GP registrar. There are, however, a growing number of schemes offering training based on 18 months as a GP registrar and 18 months in approved hospital posts.

Most GP registrars choose to do their training within a three-year structured training scheme organised through regional directors of postgraduate general practice education. Such schemes provide a series of rotations in approved hospital posts and a training practice or practices. The main advantage is that doctors do not have to find and apply for a succession of posts; they therefore enjoy a greater security of tenure and can plan their lives around the three years of training. The posts on the rotation will be approved educationally and there should be fewer problems in obtaining time off to attend relevant weekly or half-day release courses.

The other alternative is a self-constructed training programme which can offer greater flexibility in the choice and location of hospital posts. This arrangement may be particularly beneficial for doctors who are undecided about their careers and want to keep their options open. The main disadvantage is that doctors have to compete for a series of posts and must ensure that these are approved for training purposes.

Part-time training

The vocational training regulations allow part-time employment in approved training posts to qualify towards prescribed experience, provided the overall length of training is extended proportionately and that the part-time training is not less than 60% of whole time. Both the hospital and general practice components of training must also include one period of full-time employment lasting for at least a week. Part-time training should be organised in consultation with the director of postgraduate general practice education to ensure that these regulatory requirements are fulfilled.

Part-time training that does not meet the requirements for prescribed experience (for example part-time training of less than 60% of whole time) may be counted towards equivalent experience.

The GP registrar contract

During the hospital component of training doctors are employed on the normal hospital terms and conditions of employment for junior doctors. The contract governing the period of employment in general practice is a matter to be agreed between the doctor and GP trainer – there are no contractual requirements dealing with important issues such as hours of duty and holiday arrangements specified in the vocational training regulations. These and other matters should be agreed and encapsulated in a written contract of employment before a doctor takes up a post as a GP registrar. A model GP registrar contract, and advice, is available to BMA members from local offices.

However, a GP registrar's salary and a range of specific allowances to directly reimburse some of their expenses (particularly removal expenses) are detailed in the Red Book (*see* Box 16.2). The GP trainer has no discretion to vary these payments. The GP registrar's salary is fixed by reference to his or her other previous hospital posts. Thus the salary for a GP registrar who was previously a registrar in a hospital is substantially higher

---

Box 16.2: GP registrar allowances and direct reimbursements

- removal and relocation expenses (these are extensive and complex and are based on the NHS General Whitley Council conditions of service)
- travelling expenses
- interview expenses
- payments during sickness
- maternity leave payments
- expenses for postgraduate examinations

Full details are given in paragraph 38 of the Red Book.

than that paid to a doctor who was previously a SHO. A GP trainer cannot pay a GP registrar more than the appropriate salary and allowances specified in the Red Book.

Where training has to be extended because summative assessment has not been satisfactorily completed, payment of salary and allowances under the Red Book will continue for such period as has been authorised.

Payments made to the GP trainer

GP trainers are paid the following allowances and reimbursements in respect of GP registrars:

- a training grant (an allowance for the additional work and costs incurred by employing a GP registrar)
- reimbursement of the employer's share of the GP registrar's NI contributions
- a car or motor vehicle allowance, if the practice needs an additional vehicle for the GP registrar
- the costs of installing an extra telephone in the surgery and a telephone at the GP registrar's residence
- the rental charges for a telephone at the GP registrar's residence (provided the GP registrar is responsible for paying it) and the costs of installation and rental for a bedroom telephone extension at the GP registrar's home if both the health authority and trainer are satisfied that it is necessary
- the GP registrar's salary which is related to their previous hospital posts
- reimbursement of the GP registrar's medical defence subscription or premium costs, less any costs which would have been incurred had they taken out the basic subscription payable by hospital doctors (i.e. any 'additional cover' required). The GP trainer must have evidence of the GP registrar's subscription or premium being paid. The reimbursement may be paid in one lump sum or in monthly instalments to reflect the GP registrar's arrangements for paying the subscription and length of service with the trainer.

The trainer is responsible for administering the GP registrar's tax, NI and PAYE. The GP registrar's superannuation contributions are deducted from their salary. The employer's contributions are paid by the health authority.

GPs returning to practice

GPs who are exempt from the requirement to hold a certificate of prescribed or equivalent experience under the vocational training regulations or who already possess a certificate but have been absent from practice for some time and are reluctant to re-enter general practice without further training are eligible for reimbursement under the GP registrar scheme. Such doctors, although eligible to work in general practice, may be reluctant to re-enter practice without further training or experience because of a prolonged absence, for example due to home commitments or through having spent time working abroad.

Applications should be made via the director of postgraduate general practice education who will recommend a period of training not normally exceeding 12 months whole time (or its equivalent part time).

Index